HIGH-LEVEL WELLNESS

A collection of twenty-nine short talks on different
aspects of the theme "High-Level Wellness for
Man and Society"

by

HALBERT L. DUNN, M.D., Ph.D.

A Scotty Book

R. W. BEATTY, Ltd.

VIRGINIA

To
"PHELPSIE,"
my wife and co-worker

Much of the philosophy in these lectures has been tempered by the give and take, and the creative interchange of both written and spoken thought, with and among friends and colleagues interested in a common purpose and thinking along closely related lines. Were I to single out one, more than any other, to whom I feel an especial debt of gratitude in this respect, it would be John Storck, my friend and colleague during the period of most fruitful development of many of the ideas relating to the high-level wellness concept, expressed in these pages.

Jacket design by
LOUIS J. NOLAN

Graphic Art by
BERTRAND W. ADKINS

Contents

High-Level Wellness Symbol—The three interlocking orbits represent the human body as a manifestation of organized energy, and also symbolize the body, mind, and spirit of man as an interrelated and interdependent whole. The dart symbolizes the life cycle of the individual as he strives to achieve his purpose in living and grows in wholeness toward the maturity of self-fulfillment.

INTRODUCTION

The 29 short talks on various aspects of well-being contained in this book were prepared for use on the radio. This purpose called for brevity, non-technical language, and numerous illustrative examples. Consequently, the talks are suggestive rather than comprehensive in character.

Perhaps the quality of brevity in the presentations is one of the principal assets of the book, in that it has required a panoramic view of man—his nature and his physical structure, which are rooted in the laws of energy; his mind, which transcends his body through the projection and use of his imagination; his spirit, which is forged by the interaction of the energies of mind and body; and the environment, both natural and social, within which he lives out his life.

In accord with the elements of his nature, and within his environment, the individual must find his personal satisfactions and his purpose in life. These involve, among other things, the opportunity for expression of his uniqueness, and a place of dignity among his fellows.

The panoramic view of man is immense. Consequently, to see it in its wholeness and grandeur is difficult. It was not until the scripts of all 29 talks were completed and the task of compiling an index undertaken that the author became aware of the tight interrelationship and interdependence of the various parts of this book. Certain points made early in the talks are basic recurring threads which bind the whole together.

The talks have proved to be useful to educators as substance for seminar and discussion group activity. Consequently, in addition to the published sources specifically referred to in the text, a few other titles have been interspersed through the Bibliography for the benefit of the more-than-casual reader.

The theme of high-level wellness is presented as a major axis of interest which has significance to many subject fields. The philosophy is not a completed one. It needs further developing. It needs to be explored, probed, tested, questioned, and added to in all of its manifold dimensions. A broad search, interdisciplinary in character, is called for. It is my earnest hope that this small volume will play its part in stimulating such a search. HLD

———o———

"I keep six honest serving-men
 (They taught me all I knew);
 Their names are What and Why and When
 And How and Where and Who."

Just-So Stories (1902)
The Elephant's Child
—Rudyard Kipling

1. WHAT HIGH-LEVEL WELLNESS MEANS

For the first in this series of talks, I thought it would be well to look at what high-level wellness means, and why it is important to you and to me as persons. Perhaps the very best way to do this is to start with a definition of health that has been provided by the United Nations itself—that is, by the World Health Organization. This particular definition comes from the preamble of the Constitution of the World Health Organization. Here it is:

> "Health is a state of complete physical, mental, and social well-being, and not merely the absence of disease and infirmity."[1]

Now, what do these words mean? It is obvious that they mean more than just being free from sickness. Yet, most of us think that we are well when we are not sick. When we are sick, we try to get well; that is, we try to get well in the sense of being "not sick." But this World Health Organization definition means something much more than just being free of sickness. It says "a state of well-being"; that is, being well in a *positive* sense. Therefore, well-being must consist of more than a simple state of "unsickness," as it were. There must be degrees in well-being. Sometimes you are more well than at other times. Sometimes you feel all tired out. Everyone has experienced this. You aren't sick, but you lack energy; and you *make* yourself do the things that you have to do.

There are other times when you are fairly alive with the glow of good health—with wellness. Alive clear to the tips of your fingers. You have energy to burn. You tingle with vitality. At times like these, the world is a glorious place! For most of us, most of the time, we are somewhere in between these two extremes of the wellness range.

Now I would like to pose the question of what this difference means. What is it due to?

The definition of health says "complete physical, mental, and social well-being." This implies well-being both in body and mind. It includes well-being within the family and within the community life. And, it certainly includes a compatible work interest. Complete well-being calls for all of these states to happen together—wellness of the body, of the mind, and of the environment. Your body should be eager for activity. Your mind should sparkle with interest. For maximum wellness, the environment should be such as to encourage you to live life to the very full.

I cannot help but ask myself the question: Why is it that doctors and nurses and health workers so frequently forget the meaning of this definition? For, even while they quote the words, they tend to focus upon disease, disability, and death, to the exclusion of these other factors. Perhaps this is because their training has been oriented toward disease rather than toward positive wellness; and they therefore find disease more *interesting* than wellness. Also, it's easier to fight *against* sickness than to fight *for* a condition of greater wellness. After all, people—their patients—want to get well; that is, they want to be free from sickness. Yet when they are free from sickness, these same people are rarely interested in becoming more well. In short, most of us think of wellness as a single homogeneous state. As long as we view being well in this way, why should we worry about getting more well? If it's all one thing, it doesn't make any difference.

Personally, I have become deeply interested in wellness, and find it more absorbing than sickness. When we become interested in wellness as a condition, we discover that the state of being well is not just a drab, static one. Quite the contrary. It has many levels. It is ever-changing in its characteristics. In fact, it is an interrelated panorama of life itself. At times, I think of it as like the Grand Canyon. I can still remember standing on the rim of the Grand Canyon one evening, looking down as the shadows fell. Every moment the scene was changing, the colors varying. Even when night had fallen in the depth of the canyon, the interplay of light and shadow at other levels continued for long afterwards.

Well-being calls for *zest* in life. Often, we confuse zest with something that gives us a very momentary "lift." For instance, we may indulge in cocktail parties to get this lift. Some go further in their search for "kicks"—drug parties, using heroin or marijuana. But alcohol and drugs are temporary excitants. At the very best, they give a bang which is followed by a pretty severe hangover. Such excitement is not uncommonly succeeded by depression.

On the other hand, a high level of well-being brings its own lift, and has its own bang, yet it does not result in a hangover. It usually leaves a state of affairs inside of us which makes us reach for an even more zestful life, later on. We can enjoy life more because of what we *have* enjoyed.

High-level wellness is a term which has been devised to make the person who uses it think about well-being in degrees or levels. *High-Level wellness for the individual is defined as an integrated method of functioning which is oriented toward maximizing the potential of which the individual is capable. It requires that the individual maintain a continuum of balance and purposeful direction within the environment where he is functioning.*

Integrated is used in the sense of interrelated. As a baseball player, you wouldn't work just on developing your arm muscles, because you had to pitch. You would develop your whole body. You would be in good condition from every angle. Most of us don't care too much for the person who has developed in a lopsided way—for the athlete who is a "dumb bunny," or the beautiful girl who is a bore. All of us need balance in our lives. We need to be well-rounded people.

The term *maximizing* in this definition has a sense similar to the term *complete,* used in the definition of health by the World Health Organization. However, there is one important difference between the word complete, and the word maximizing. The latter implies *maintaining* completeness. When you stop to think of it, what is complete today might be quite incomplete tomorrow. But *maximizing* means maintaining completeness from day to day. Or, looking at it another way, *complete* is a static word; *maximizing* is a dynamic word, a *becoming* word.

What about the word *potential?* Potential, in the definition, stands for what one is *capable* of doing. All of us have our physical and mental limitations, but our *potential* is the very best that we can do, within these limitations.

In using this definition of wellness, I do not wish

to imply that there is an optimum level of wellness, but rather that wellness is a *direction in progress* toward an ever-higher potential of functioning. Neither do I wish to put a limit on the way or the degree to which the individual is able to function, with respect to particular body parts. Rather, I'd like to imply that it involves *the total individual* as a personality *in all of his uniqueness*.

At the beginning of this talk, I posed the question of why this concept of high-level wellness is important to you and to me. Fundamentally, it is because the world is changing so fast. The reason for the change, primarily, is the phenomenal progress of science. Science has brought us so many things, in so short a period of time. The telephone and the radio and television have shrunk communication throughout the world to a matter of seconds or minutes. Travel time from anywhere to anywhere is a matter of minutes or days, at most. Food and living necessities are more abundant, at least in the industrialized nations. And, medicine and public health are saving lives on an unprecedented scale. This, together with birth rate factors, has resulted in a tremendous population increase, growing by leaps and bounds throughout the world. But population density and the patterns of industrial and urban development have brought increased tensions and social problems, into almost every facet of daily living.

The concept of high-level wellness—in the individual, the family, the community—embodies the *preventive aspects* of many of the things which we are now fighting in terms of disease and disability and social breakdown. Patching up is no longer sufficient. This is why high-level wellness is important to you and to me, and to the larger groups of which we are a part.

2. THE NATURE OF MAN

In my last talk, I said that high-level wellness involves several things—first of all, a direction in progress forward and upward toward a higher potential of functioning; second, an open-ended and ever-expanding tomorrow, with its challenge to live at a fuller potential; and third, the integration of the whole being of the individual, of the total individual—his body, his mind, his spirit—in the functioning process.

Today, we shall examine the question of whether or not the nature of man is consistent with such a definition. Of course, all of us think of man's nature in different ways. I can't help but remember the little poem that we learned in childhood about what little boys were made of: snips, and snails, and puppy dog tails. I can remember thinking that the definition of little girls was much nicer: sugar, and spice, and everything nice. And, for quite a while, as a little boy, I went around wondering about those puppy dog tails and how we could be made out of such material.

Most of us tend to think of people in terms of stereotypes, interpreting them as reflections of human nature. The man is a brute, or the woman is a shrew, or the child is a brat. Not long ago, I was talking with a certain person about war, and his statement was, "Why, there'll always be wars, because it is a part of the nature of man to go to war." Well, I can't agree with him, but it does seem to me that nature in these terms is *not* what we are talking about here.

The basis for high-level wellness as a useful concept in daily living lies in the nature of man. It would seem to me that there are five major factors in the nature of man which need consideration: First of all, his totality, the fact that he functions as a total personality; second, his uniqueness, the realization that there is nobody else like him in the whole world; third, the enormous amount of energy at his disposal, because his body is a manifestation of organized energy; fourth, the inner and the outer worlds in which he lives and with which he must make his peace; and finally, the interrelation of self-integration and energy use.

Let us first consider the individual as a *total personality*. I think of the person as a continuum of body and mind and spirit, which is functioning within an ever-changing environment and flow of events. Now, by body and mind and spirit, I am thinking of these as a total blending. Most of us think of the body as something which is physical, the mind as something we don't quite know what it is, and the spirit as something which is outside the body and mind. Yet, we physicians for the most part have come to realize that the spirit is something very real, that it involves the process of healing, and that we can't shrug it off as something for the churches and the ministers alone. It must be a concern also of the doctor. The reason for this is that we have frequently observed people with a sick body but a well spirit, and, when this is true, such people try to get well and they frequently do get well. But we seldom see a person with a sick spirit who has a well body.

It is equally true that we cannot consider body, mind, and spirit of the individual without also thinking about the environment in which he is functioning. The environment makes a lot of difference. It can be very favorable, and if it is, that suits our purposes. If it's too unfavorable, death will ensue. If it is too favorable, on the other hand, we are inclined to become vegetables and do nothing. It is necessary for our environment to have something in it which challenges the spirit and the mind, so that we function at our very best. Unless there is a reason for living, unless there is purpose in our life, we cannot possibly achieve high-level wellness.

Now, the second factor in the nature of man which is important to high-level wellness is his *uniqueness*. Each of us is unique. Each exhibits his individuality in his body, his mind, and his spirit. Just stop and think—in the whole history of the world, there has never been a person exactly like you. In the entire world today, and in all of the people to come in this world, there will never be anybody completely like you. This uniqueness which is yours must find an expression, because it is reflected not only in your body, mind, and spirit, and in your total personality, but it is also a part of the tissues of your body, of the cells of your body, of the fluids of your body. Roger Williams, who has done much work in this area, has made this statement on the point:

> "Every newborn baby has a distinctive and complex pattern of inborn mental capacities. Each item in this pattern is derived from his human forebears, but the pattern with its interactions is unique." [2]

As we strive for self-fulfillment in this life of ours, let us never forget that there must be an expression for our uniqueness. Self-fulfillment cannot be found just in terms of families, or organizations, or work; it must be found, at least in part, through an expression of the uniqueness which is our very own.

The third factor in connection with the nature of man, which must be taken into account in high-level wellness, is the fact that *he is made of energy*.

That's right. I mean that every part of the tissues of his body is a manifestation of organized energy. After all, this should not be so strange an idea, because we now know that everything in the universe that is material is made of energy: the atoms, the molecules, the chemicals, and the living substances of our body. It follows that since we are made of energy, we must recognize the laws of energy in connection with our bodies. We must have our food, and we must have oxygen from the air, because these are the major sources of the energy for our body.

Some of the energy we take into our body cannot be used. This becomes waste matter and must be discarded. Certain energies are harmful to our body. These, for the most part, come from the outside world. They are represented by such things as bacteria, poisons, toxic substances of all kinds. Recently, we've become worried about radiation in the atmosphere, because radiation can be harmful and can tear down the body cells. Body cells are also subjected, at times, to destructive energy from the inside of the body, resulting in psychosomatic illness. We'll deal with that later in this series of talks.

In concluding our remarks on energy, let us recognize that energy systems are never static. Energy never stands still. Either it is building into a more complex form that is more efficient, or it is tearing down and retreating. Since energy is dynamic, and the body is made of energy, any concept of wellness must be dynamic.

The fourth major facet in man's nature which needs consideration is that we all *live in both an inner and an outer world*. To our inner world, there are ports of entry, ports through which we take our food and oxygen and other sources of energy, and get rid of waste products; and ports which bring in information. Information that is brought into the body is then stored in the tissues; it is organized and reused and tried out; and once it is tried out and found to work, it becomes experience upon which we can build and run our lives.

I won't go into the matter, now, of using our minds and bodies for problem-solving, because other talks in this series will deal with that subject. Suffice it to say that we take the values which we have—values which are tuned into whether things are good or bad for us, we make judgments, we use our imagination, we develop a concept of our self and a concept of what the outer world is, and out of all this, we build our way of life. The entire play of life is conducted as an exchange between the inner and the outer world. And, the way we conduct ourselves in the outer world depends very largely upon what we store within the inner world and use as our perception of what we should do in the outer world.

The final factor of man's nature which needs discussion as a part of high-level wellness is the fact that there is *interrelationship between self-integration and the way we use physical energy.* If we have integrated ourself, integrated all of our experience into a body of knowledge upon which we can operate, upon which we can run our life well, then we use the physical energy at the disposal of our body in a *good* way.

To summarize: The nature of man embraces his totality, and his uniqueness. He is a child of energy, and must obey its laws. He lives in both an inner and an outer world. And finally, he must achieve self-integration, if he is to use the physical energy at his disposal safely and effectively.

3. MAN AS A MANIFESTATION OF ENERGY

Today, I thought that we might examine more closely one of the points made in the second talk, on "The Nature of Man." I know that our title, "Man as a Manifestation of Energy," sounds rather formidable, but it does seem to me that we cannot really understand the importance of high-level wellness unless we understand why man is an organization of energy—really a child of energy.

Now, what is energy? One of my friends who is a physicist, and a good one, asked me after listening to some of my talks, "Why is it, Dunn, that you base all of your philosophy upon the greatest mystery of all?" I said, "Well, what do you mean by that?" His response was, "Energy, after all, is the one thing in the whole universe we haven't any idea as to what it really is."

We do know, or at least we can assume, that energy has an unorganized form. As a matter of fact, the assumption goes that unorganized energy fills most of space, and it is only when space becomes too full of such energy that part of it is squeezed out into organized forms which make up the material universe in which we live. However, it *is* a mystery, and probably the only comparable mystery is, "what is consciousness?"

There's not much doubt—in my mind, at least—that creative consciousness is an undifferentiated unity which permeates all of the known universe, and all of the space and reaches of unorganized energy outside of the known universe. This will be touched on more fully at a later point. What we need to do now is to consider the possibilities and the meaning of man as a child of energy. Even though energy may be a mystery to us, it has some very definite laws, and man must obey these laws.

Now, the types of energy within the body, I have grouped roughly into five major classes: Energy bound into matter; energy bound into form; communication energy; stored energy; expendable energy.

The first of these, *bound energy,* is bound into the material substances which make up our body; that is, into the water, the salts, and other chemicals of the body. We know that salt, for instance, is contained in our body in substantial quantity, and we know that it is essentially the same form as salt anywhere else. The water, nitrogen—all of these kinds of materials which go into the chemical substances of our body—I am classifying, for want of a better name, as energy bound into matter.

As life emerges in the form of protoplasm, a great deal of energy goes into the creation of a higher form of matter. It is through this second type of energy, which we shall call *energy bound into form,* that we link the various chemical substances together so as to make form in terms of cellular structures.

There is a third type of energy, which I'm calling *communication energy.* It is the energy required inside the body to keep the cells and the various systems in relationship with one another. This communication is a constant phenomenon, and undoubtedly, a large amount of it is required. Dr. Hans Selye, of Canada, who is a well-known medical investigator, calls this *adaptation energy.* And, in his book *The Stress of Life,* he says this about adaptation energy:

> "It is as though, at birth, each individual inherited a certain amount of adaptation energy, the magnitude of which is determined by his genetic background. . . . He can draw upon this capital thriftily for a long but monotonously uneventful existence, or he can spend it lavishly in the course of a stressful, intense, but perhaps more colorful and exciting life. In any case, there is just so much of it, and he must budget accordingly."[3]

Certainly, as we grow older, this communication energy is something that we must give greater consideration to, because it is absolutely necessary to keep the body working together in wholeness. And, unquestionably, part of the aging process is the diminution of this type of energy, because we have used up so much of it in our earlier years.

A fourth kind of energy is stored in various types of tissues. The most important example of *stored energy* is fat, of which many of us have a surplus, because we like our food so much. But part of the energy that is surplus is stored in other ways. It goes into various types of secretions, into the hormones of our body, into glycogen in our liver, and the like. We call upon these sources of energy when we need them; that is, when we aren't getting enough of a certain type of element in our daily food to take care of current energy needs.

The fifth kind of energy, which I'm calling *expendable energy,* is very important to us. This we use in our daily activities. We need it in abundance, and use it prodigally. Fortunately, the more well we are, the more expendable energy we seem to have in our bodies, available for our purposes. It's sort of like the electrical energy in a battery, which, in the form of chemical potential, fills the whole battery. When we turn it on for a particular purpose—say, to give light, it burns intensively to do this job. Of course, if we burn our light all the time, then the battery runs down pretty fast. It is quite likely that we sleep at night in part because we need to recharge the "battery" of our body so as to have a sufficient amount of energy in our daylight hours.

I would like to devote the remaining time available to *energy fields*. First, what is an energy field? It is a space traversed by lines of force. We are familiar with magnetic fields, because we know how magnets work. We are also, most of us, familiar with electrical fields. We probably do not think of *social energy fields,* but from the standpoint of lines of influence, they are very much a part of high-level wellness. We probably also have *personality energy fields*.

To understand better what an energy field is, let us look at one of the smallest forms of matter, the atom. The energy field of each atom is relatively vast in its dimensions. It binds within it huge quantities of space. To gain some idea of the relative distance involved, imagine the nucleus of a hydrogen atom to be a mile in diameter. The electron held by its polarized electrostatic field of force would be whirling about the nucleus, approximately a hundred thousand miles away from it. Yet, all of this relatively vast reach of space would be ruled largely by the influence of a single energy field.

As atoms are built into molecules, new energy fields are created. They have polarities of their own, with new reaches of space bound within them. These energy fields overlap and interpenetrate each other. For instance, the energy field of an atom, under certain conditions, moves about or moves through the energy field of a molecule, and, in its course, affects the containing fields of influence, undergoing and causing certain stresses and strains.

It seems to me that it is just such processes as these which influence the fundamental quality of uniqueness inside of people. Some of the electrons at the periphery of a particular energy field are torn away, when they approach another energy field. Now, they can't just vanish into nothingness. So, they team up with some other break-away unit, and create a new substance. This simply underscores how important uniqueness is, because always the hope for doing something better, something new, for making progress in the future, depends upon recognizing the importance of uniqueness.

The building substance of life is protoplasm. This complex chemical arrangement is able to extract energy from the environment and use it for its purposes. From protoplasm, the basic building substance, living cells are formed. And from these, all multicellular life structures are built. Man is perched precariously at the apex of this life process. He is master of the larger animals of the world, but frequently is in open warfare with the tiniest of living structures—in particular, with the germs and the viruses.

High-level wellness involves an interrelatedness of energy fields. This is the reason why man must face up to the fact that he is a child of energy. If we are to have high-level wellness, these energy fields must reinforce one another. They must interlock, instead of being destructive of one another.

One last thought. At certain moments in time, the direction which energy fields take can be influenced by very delicate forces. It is my view that when energy fields come into balance, the thought process itself can affect the direction which the energy fields will then take. This is the reason why *purpose in life* is so very important to human beings.

4. THE INNER AND THE OUTER WORLDS

꧅

In this talk I would like to return to one of the points made earlier, in "The Nature of Man"; that is, that man lives in both an inner and an outer world. The inner world is the world made up of the cells of his body—considered as an organized whole. The outer world is the one in which he exists and to which he must adjust if he is to enjoy well-being.

Each person must find his being and his belonging with reference to both his inner world and the position in which he finds himself in the outer world. He must find an answer to at least these four questions: What am I? Where am I? Where am I going? Why am I?

Now, it would be very difficult to answer these questions unless we have a concept of ourselves in relation to both an inner and an outer world.

You know, this concept came very late in the evolution of the animal kingdom. It would not appear, for instance, that the birds or any of the higher animals have it. Only man seems to have it.

I get a great deal of enjoyment out of seeing the mockingbird in our yard. He loves to sing, particularly in the spring when he is feeling good. He'll get up on top of a tall pole or the roof of the house, and when he reaches for high notes he raises up on his toes in order to get to that note. Now, it seems to me that this mockingbird feels himself as actually the note that he is reaching for. He doesn't think of himself as something different from the note.

We humans, on the other hand, have the capacity to think of ourselves as an inner world—a self that is different from the world around us. This realization grows rather slowly. The baby isn't born with it. At first, the baby, lying in the crib, waves his hands and is not quite sure whether his hands are a part of his body or not. He reaches out for a light that is over him, which may be on the ceiling, but he reaches for it as though it might be a part of him.

In the first two or three months, the baby probably thinks of his mother as a part of himself. After all, every time he cries, she does something for him. He has more control over her than he has over his hands. But eventually, he gets to the place where he knows that he is a separate *being*. And, this leads him to the second step.

He realizes that if he is a separate someone, then everything else must be something else. Therefore, he's a part of something. He's a part of something bigger. He *belongs* to something. And, as this realization comes to pass, then he reaches out. He tries to develop. He starts to adventure, and he realizes that, "Well, I'm going somewhere. I'm developing. I'm growing. I'm *becoming.*"

As he grows and matures, he begins to pick and choose. He becomes selective. In effect, he says, "I am steering my course. I'm choosing. I'm selecting. I'm fitting myself. I am *befitting.*"

Now, these four *spatial* terms—being, belonging, becoming, befitting—which I think of as the four "B's," I have borrowed from Ross Mooney, a good friend at Ohio State University.

Another dimension in this physical universe in which we find ourselves, which I should like to discuss, is *time.*

Time is the direction we follow as we go through life. This being that I am is an open system. It's always exchanging energy and information, in and out, with what is about me. The cells of my body are open systems too. The family that I'm in—it is an open system. It is always changing. It is becoming. It is befitting. And the community that I'm in, the society that I'm in, mankind as a whole—they're all open systems. They are all moving through time. All are changing.

So, the four "W" questions that I asked at the beginning of this talk—"What am I? Where am I?

Where am I going? And, Why am I?"—are matched up with the four "B" statements. I am a being. I belong to something bigger. I am becoming something, as I go through life. And, I am befitting. I am fitting myself to do what I should do in connection with all that is about me.

Is this all there is to life and to living? Is this the whole story? It is for the animal kingdom, but it is not for mankind. With the emergence of the mind, man has found it possible to obtain information for his inner world from the outer. He takes this information. He organizes it. He tries it out. And, he builds it into a plan of life and living. This means that we never get through learning. Insofar as our mind goes, we are always growing. The process of growing is a continuous flow—always changing, always making new interpretations, always becoming. All life is a becoming.

Probably the most important thing of all about us—the thing that really makes us distinct from the rest of the animals—is that we have an imagination. This imagination represents the breakthrough in the use of the mind by man with respect to his ability to solve problems. As we work on the things which interest us, as we dedicate ourselves, this imagination takes on a creative character; and creative imagination, in my opinion, is the very greatest asset that man has for his future. It is where he has the greatest perception outward and the greatest insight into himself. It draws heavily on information gathered from the outside world; yet it does not exclude fantasy, because it is in part an outgrowth of fantasy and the early imaginings of childhood.

Later, we will talk further about creative imagination and its particular role in the scheme of our existence. It is what gives the zip and zing to life. And, when it is suppressed, it takes its toll from the body.

Before closing this talk, there is one point I want to bring out about the inner world. It is that there is a very real and important relationship between the way we use our mind and the way we use the energy at the disposal of our body. There is a two-way functional relationship between the body as an energy organization and man's awareness of what he is and what he is becoming. Self-integration—that is, the interweaving of all that we know about ourselves and about life—must be of a degree sufficient to enable us to operate as a whole. If we can't maintian self-integration, then we start going to pieces pretty fast. We get sick, and this is what the doctors call psychosomatic illness, because the very fact that we are not self-integrated means that some of the energy, the physical energy at our disposal, starts to tear down the tissues of the body.

It is up to us, therefore, to become aware of the need for purpose in life. Security cannot be achieved just by crawling into a little box of fixed beliefs.

If something comes along and breaks the box up, then, there we are, all naked and unprotected. So, we really must—if we wish security—achieve a degree of self-integration.

Now, we can't achieve self-integration and purpose through a static position in a dynamic world. This integration must be a dynamic equilibrium—one that is undergoing a continuity of change. The principal hope that we have for the conquest of space and time, and of energy and matter, is through a release of this quality that has come to us as an outgrowth of the mind of man—man's spirit, the creative imagination which can soar without limits, and which can bring purpose into our lives.

In closing, I would like to postulate, then, that the mind of man is an open system, too; that the creative imagination of man has broken the rigid shackles of time itself; and that purpose, as it has emerged—a dominant factor in achieving wellness of the mind—has become a rival of time. With purpose, the mind of man can do anything. It can go anywhere. It can answer the question *why*. Why am I? Why is man?

5. THE NATURE AND THE NEEDS OF CELLS

In the talk today, I thought we would take up something about the nature and needs of cells—body cells, that is.

Now, every type of cell is made of what we call protoplasm. And, protoplasm has some very definite qualities. Among these qualities are: irritability, motility, metabolism, growth, reproduction, and adaptability. Protoplasm, of course, is not only the basis for development of human life, but it also furnishes the building substance for all types of life in the vegetable kingdom and the animal kingdom. Thus, from protoplasm we have, in the form of cells, the building blocks for all living matter.

I would like to consider, first, the nature of the cell taken as a whole. When you consider it as a whole, it is very much like the nature of man, which we considered in the second talk of this series. First of all, man is a tremendous organization of cells. And the cell, in its turn, is a tremendous organization of molecules. From the standpoint of sheer numbers, the cell rules over a domain of molecules as vast as the domain of cells which the body rules over. Actually, if one tried to calculate the number of molecules, there are probably a hundred thousand million of them in the average cell. This is an unbelievably huge domain.

Just as individuals have to be considered as a whole, and just as each individual is a completely unique personality in his own right, the cell must be considered as a unique totality in its own right. The cell is made of energy, just as man is made of energy. And the cell has an inner and an outer world. All cells are open systems. Their outer world consists of a ground substance, composing the fluids of the blood and plasma which bathes them. From these fluids, the cells get the things they need and reject into the fluids the things that they don't want.

Now, the cells are also an ordered world. They have within them a lot of means by which they can do things; but they must remain an ordered world if they are to use efficiently the energy available to them.

Let us now look at the nature of the cell inside. Since the cell is made of protoplasm, we need to think of it in terms of the basic qualities of protoplasm. The first of these was *irritability*. And, by irritability, I mean the ability to attract or to repel. Probably some of you have looked at the antics of an amoeba on the microscopic stage. If you haven't, you should do so, because you can see the amoeba approaching a tiny little crumb of substance, which it either likes or it doesn't like. If the amoeba likes the substance, it flows around it; if it doesn't like it, it flows away from it. Well, this is what the quality of irritability has given it. And, I suppose, of all the cells that are involved with irritability, the nerve cell is the most highly specialized in this respect.

The brain, which is composed mostly of nerve cells, can remember all sorts of things—for instance, a telephone number, the color of a dress, an odor. How can this be? Somehow, in some fashion, a few of the molecules inside the cell are subtly changed or rearranged, and this change will carry the memory of, say, a telephone number. This is really an astounding process. A molecule—which is made of carbon and hydrogen, nitrogen and oxygen, and some sulphur atoms—apparently makes a minute rearrangement of its constituent atoms as the telephone number is funneled into the cell. The rearrangement serves as a code, and, when you want the information again, the code is activated. A mysterious series of events translates the stored information into the digits that give commands to your eyes and ears so that you can dial that number on the telephone. This

34

extraordinary process is what you might call molecular memory.

The second quality of protoplasm, *motility*, is something that our body cells don't have too much of. They, for the most part, have given up the right to move about, so as to be able to cooperate with one another. This is not entirely true, of course; some of the cells move about a great deal. Take, for instance, the reticulo-endothelial cells, which are the policemen of the body. It's their job to get about everywhere and protect the body. That's a large order.

Suppose you had the job of policing all of the people of the world. This would mean that you were pretty flexible and pretty motile. Well, that's exactly what the reticulo-endothelial cells are. They're there to protect us—to protect us against infections and foreign substances, and they're very largely responsible for man's resistance to disease. All of us know, for example, that there are bacteria all around us—in the air we breathe, in the things we touch—and it is these particular little cells which are responsible for resisting invasion of bacteria into our bodies.

How do the reticulo-endothelial cells do this? Well, first of all, they have been taught to recognize the characteristics of the body proteins of the person whose organization they are a part of. Consequently, they can recognize foreign substances and proceed

to attack them ruthlessly. These little cellular policemen of ours form a great defensive army. As long
as the army is strong and well developed, a person
stays healthy; but, if it is weakened or if the invasion
force is so massive that it comes in through a broad
infection that overwhelms the cells, then we have to
turn for help to various types of medication, as, for
example, antibiotics.

The third quality that the cell has is *metabolism*.
All the cells are little factories, and they have some
amazing equipment to use in these factories. They
have literally thousands of chemical instruments.
They're called enzymes, but they're very specific
tools. Each tool is designed to do a special chemical
job, and all are kept ready for use when needed.
The factories are very highly specialized, and do
different kinds of work. Take the thyroid cells in
the thyroid glands, for instance. Their job is to
make thyroxine. Well, thyroxine needs iodine, so
the thyroid cells are on the lookout for iodine in the
food, in whatever form. They pluck out the iodine
and put it to use.

And, there are the kidney cells. We'd be in quite
a fix if the kidney cells weren't always on the lookout
for the valuable things that we need in our body.
Out of all the waste that comes to them, they pick the
good things that we need, and route them right back
into the blood stream. Without the kidney cells, we
would really be in pretty bad shape.

Well, I can't begin to tell you the extent of the specialization of the cells. They're well disciplined, too. They regulate themselves. If we could even begin to have as well-ordered a society, if we could be disciplined within it to the degree that our cells are within the body, it would be a well-run society indeed!

Growth is another factor inherent in the nature **of a cell. Life starts as soon as the ovum is fertilized,** and goes through an enormous course of growth through cell division, until the mature individual emerges. As life proceeds, things happen in what we call a time sequence—a maturation as it were. "Maturation" is used here in the sense of a process where time, as it has been built into the hereditarial inheritance of the cell, takes over and causes certain things to happen when they should happen. Eventually, as the individual matures, there is so much wear and tear in the body that the matter of replacement becomes a paramount concern to the cells, and, finally, they have to use most of their energy just in holding things together.

Reproduction, of course, involves the whole matter of heredity, and is entirely too vast a subject to treat here. We'll make it the subject of a separate talk.

Adaptability is the sixth quality of protoplasm which has very great meaning to our cells, particularly to those cells which serve as chemical factories. The fact that cells can adapt makes it possible for them to enjoy interdependence with other cells, interdependence so that they can get along together as an organized whole.

We haven't yet discussed the *needs* of cells. But, the needs must be recognized if we're going to have well-being of the cells of our body. Primarily, these needs are chemical. We must have good oxygen and proper foods with the chemicals in them which are needed by the cells of the body. We must avoid the poisons which tear down the cells. We must avoid the excessive use of tranquilizers, and drugs, and alcohol, as well as other things that the cells can't take too much of.

The cells also need certain electrical components. They are bathed in the fluids of the ground substance upon which they rest. There must be a proper balance between negative and positive ions, if the materials are to move in and out of the cells properly. All of us have felt the exhilaration that comes before a storm, when the air seems to be purified. At such times, the air is full of negative ionization. The resulting effect is a cellular exhilaration.

We should pay tribute to the body cells. They are doing a magnificent job. If we give them the things they need, these indefatigable little soldiers will do their very best for us.

6. THE CELLULAR COMMONWEALTH

Last time, we discussed the nature and the needs of body cells. This time, I'd like to talk about the way these cells work together. I'm calling today's talk "the cellular commonwealth.' This is a good name, in my opinion, because "commonwealth" comes from *commonweal* or "common welfare," the general good, as it were.

How would you like to be in charge of all the people in the world? Well, this is the order of vastness of the cellular commonwealth of which you are actually in charge. In fact, the hundred trillion cells far outnumber the people in the world. It would actually take about 37 thousand worlds of the type that we have, each one with about the same number of people in it as our world has now, to equal the total number of cells in the body.

How would you go about ruling a world of this size, with this degree of complexity? Would you do it as a dictator? Would you try to make it a democracy? What sort of leadership would you exercise? Well, one thing I'm pretty sure you would have to do, no matter what form of government—you would have to understand your domain well.

As I see it, there are certain problems faced by this commonwealth of cells that is ours. It is organized into systems, and there are certain functions performed by each of the systems. Let us look at the problems, the systems, the functions, and then come back to management.

The problems start with survival. The commonwealth is no good at all unless it can survive. Survival means primarily having sufficient energy for the purposes of the commonwealth, getting rid of the energy that it has no use for, and protecting itself from energy which is harmful to it.

The second major problem faced by the commonwealth of cells is gravitational effects and surface tensions. These are physical phenomena, but they are very important to growth, maturation (the automatic process of physical development built into our cells), and the maturing of the individual in other ways. D'Arcy Thompson, in his classic book, *Growth and Form*, pictures the massive effect which is played by gravity on the various types of life forms. At the top of the animal kingdom, he places the large whale. Then comes the elephant, then various other mammals. From man, who is in an intermediate position, he goes down through the smaller animals—the dog, the rat, most birds, the insects. Finally, there are the bacteria and the viruses. As the size lessens, the effect of gravity decreases, and the effect of surface tensions becomes greater.

Thompson brings out the fact that in the growth of the individual from a single cell to an adult, the surface area cannot keep pace with volume. Thus, as it grows through various periods of life from a unicellular condition to the mature individual, the cellular commonwealth has a whole new set of problems, revolving largely around how to hold together a constantly increasing size against the pressures of the environment around it. This, for example, accounts for the interfolding of the surface of the brain as the individual approaches maturity.

Much of the problem is involved with communication. How do you manage to stay organized when you get larger and larger? Even the social organization as it grows larger faces this kind of problem, and finds it very difficult to solve. Suffice it to say that the cellular commonwealth finds communication difficult even under the best of circumstances.

In order to serve the commonwealth better, the cells are organized into systems. These are the digestive system; the respiratory system; the vascular system, which includes heart, blood vessels, and the lymphatics; the muscular system; the nervous system; the endocrine system; and the skeletal system.

There is not time to discuss the details of these systems. In fact, that is the whole area of the subject of physiology.

Now, there are a number of functions which must be performed by these various systems, if the cellular commonwealth is to be well served. First of all, I suppose, we should list the relationships with the outer world. There are ports of entry and exit for energy and information, and these must be kept open and adequately maintained. This is primarily the function of the digestive, respiratory, and nervous systems.

The next most important function is, undoubtedly, that of the transformation of energy. This involves the cells, primarily, although the cells which are involved may be scattered through quite a number of the system of the body. Transportation of energy and waste is a function that is going on all the time. Primarily, it involves the vascular system; but it also involves the muscles which make the vessels work, and the nerve fibers as well as the digestive and endocrine systems.

There are two functions performed by the body which involve all of the systems of the body working together. The first of these is growth. It goes without saying that everything is involved in this process of growth—every part of the body and every cell of the body. The second of these generalized functions involves the adjustments which are going on all the time with reference to various types of energy fields. We've already mentioned in this talk the necessity for the growing body to conform with gravitational effects—a universal force field. There are almost unlimited numbers of other energy fields, both inside and outside of the body, to which adjustment must be made continually.

Reproduction is a very specialized function which we won't touch on here because it will be the subject of a later talk. We have already mentioned that one of the great problems faced by the cellular commonwealth is communication. This important function is handled by a number of the systems of the body, primarily, of course, the nervous system, but also the vascular system. And, the muscles enter very heavily into this picture. Even the cells participate because, as we have already seen, this is where the chemical types of memories are stored.

Problem-solving is probably the most important function faced by the cellular commonwealth. This function includes the storage of information in various parts of the body, and its integration and use. The two systems of the body primarily concerned with problem-solving are the nervous system and the muscular system. A great deal of the information that we have, that we think of as experience, is stored in the muscle fibers themselves. The difficult matter of keeping the body working together as a whole—that is, the matter of control—is carried out jointly by the muscles and nerves. In fact, a good share of the controlling function is turned over to the autonomic nervous system.

This particular branch of the nervous system— the autonomic—is made up of the so-called sympathetic and parasympathetic nerves. These are the nerve supply of the smooth muscle fibers of the body—that is, the fibers which makes the arteries and the intestines work, which dilate and contract the pupil of the eyes, and that sort of thing. There is a nerve of each type—sympathetic and parasympathetic—going to every smooth muscle fiber. One turns the fiber on and the other turns it off. For instance, the sympathetic system dilates the pupil of the eye, and the parasympathetic system constricts it.

Before closing this talk, I should like to draw a parallel about communication, in every-day terms that you, as an audience, can understand. Unless the true significance of open channels of communication in the life process becomes broadly appreciated, social man is spelling out his own doom. The cells and the systems of the body simply must work together. They cannot favor one part over another. If these cells and these systems of our body were operated in the same fashion as social man now operates, the various types of tissues and glandular substances would probably organize as "pressure groups" so as to present their favored views, and suppress unfavored ones. They would attempt to cut off the data needed by the individual to solve his daily problems in the best interest of the body as a whole. Inevitably, body, mind, and spirit would sicken and die in the resulting chaos of the conflicting energy fields set up.

So, in the end, the problem come down to management, because the principal problem faced by the cellular commonwealth is how to maintain unity as a whole. This is where you and I come in, with the "I" that is somewhere inside of our body and mind. We need to rule this body of ours, not as a despot over a vassal state, but as a leader of a cellular commonwealth. We need to respect the cells. We need to take their dissatisfactions to heart. We need to give them the things essential to their well-being. If we're good leaders, we'll find out what they want and do the very best we can to give it to them.

So, my final question is, "How good a leader are you? How well are you handling your commonwealth of cells?"

7. THE LIFE CYCLE

In the preceding talk on "The Cellular Common-wealth," we touched on growth. The present talk concerns the life cycle, the period between conception and death during which we live out our lives.

Life, for the individual, commences with the fertilization of the ovum. Heredity, contributed by the father and the mother, plays its part by passing on to the new individual the principal biological factors received from the race. The building plan for any new life form is carried in a codescript, a four-dimensional codescript, which is contained within the chromosomes and the genes of the fertilized ovum. Three of the dimensions of the codescript are required for the production of the various forms and shapes of the body, and the fourth carries a message of time. This timing message is called "maturation." An example of it might be the development of the sexual organs, which wait until puberty. Thus, at the start of puberty, the body must receive some sort of a message which tells it to start this type of development.

Now, the growth of the body takes place through successive cell divisions. The fertilized ovum divides into two parts, and these two parts into two more, so that four cells are produced; and then in successive divisions, 8 cells, 16 cells, 32 cells, etc. If it were not for attrition taking place in the divided cells, fifty generations of dividing cells would suffice for the creation of the entire body of the individual.

Is it not an interesting fact that through each of these cellular divisions, this four-dimensional code-script is reproduced intact? That is, the pattern of the chromosomes and genes which have been produced by the fusion of the mother's and father's characteristics in the fertilized ovum are passed on to every cell of the body. This is an amazing device. If we were building a house, for instance, it would be more or less as though the complete blueprints of the house were incorporated into every stick and stone and brick that was used to build the house.

Just what this phenomenon signifies—just what part it may play in the process of maturation, nobody knows. Perhaps this is nature's way of ensuring the degree of unquestioned cellular instruction needed to bind the body together into a commonwealth of cells, and to ensure cooperation of the whole.

If this is the beginning of life, what is death? Death would seem to be a phenomenon of the cellular organism taken as a whole. The body can die; but small parts of it, such as transplants of certain cells, may be kept alive in tissue culture for a considerable period of time. One is forced to the conclusion that aging of the individual is actually a manifestation of the *breakdown in the cooperation between body cells*. The growing body is a topological structure, and when this structure eventually breaks, death results.

This term "topological" is going to appear numerous times in our talks, and perhaps we should stop right here and define it. By topological structure, I mean a structure or an organization that can change its specific size and shape without tearing or breaking apart, or without combining with other structures or organizations into some new form. Death to the individual, therefore, occurs when the topological structure breaks.

Now, let us briefly review the stages or periods of growth that the individual goes through. These are nine in number: incubation, emergence, the sheltered nook period, growing up, puberty—or entering into adulthood—the principal productive years, the start of physical decline, the calmer years, and dissolution.

During *incubation*, the sole function of the embryo and the fetus is to grow. Protected in the warm security of intra-uterine life, the embryo is largely isolated from the shocks and impressions of the outer world. Its task is to grow, and to do this it must extract energy brought to it through the mother's circulation of blood and transform the energy into living cells through mitosis and cell division. The mother's diet, therefore, is of very great importance to the fetus. Her diet must have in it the foods which are rich in protein, iron, calcium and vitamines. Milk, cheese, lean beef, poultry, fish, and eggs supply the needed proteins, calcium, and iron. Vitamines and ready energy come from fruits and vegetables, and from cereals.

Emergence at birth is the first of three major transformations made during the life cycle—the other two being puberty and menopause. The process of birth transforms the fetus from an aquatic form of life to an air-breathing one. Birth is a very distressing experience to the baby, because the intra-uterine environment of the fetus is placid, calm, secure, and warm, whereas the experience of birth is traumatic and painful. To the newborn, the world outside seems harsh and cruel in contrast to the snug security afforded within the uterus.

This is one reason why the first three months after birth, which we shall call the *sheltered nook period*, are so very important to the child. During this period, he must feel secure and safe; otherwise, the outside world would appear formidable to him. He would be afraid—more or less continuously—and this fear could remain with him even after he became an adult. And, it is the basic reason why mother love is so important during this period.

There is really no substitute for mother love, to make the outer world seem attractive and safe. Unfortunate is the infant who cannot learn about life from the vantage point of such a haven—who cannot know the security of mother love as a starting point from which to adventure in safety, who cannot have the experience of *belonging,* while entering the world of *becoming.*

The *period of growing up,* which stretches between the third month of life and puberty, is the period during which the child must become both humanized and socialized if he is to fulfill his role later in the adult society. This is a period, therefore, of gradual unfolding; first within the protective limitations of the family circle, then within the confines of a community in which the family lives, and, finally, at school and throughout the wider ranges of social living. The child who first learns about other people through the loving concern of family members is able later to go out into society protected by a shield of love, a shield which is lowered, little by little, until he is finally on his own.

Puberty marks the fifth stage in the life of man. It involves both a biological and a social element. Biologically, it means that he can now conceive and rear children. Socially, it means that the time has come for him to assume a responsible role in the adult world. The adolescent period is marked by insecurity and awkwardness. The main questions which dominate this time of life are of this order: "What is the meaning of sex?" "What is my part in relation to propagation?" "What is life all about anyway?" "Why am I here?" "What makes life worth while?" So, if we are to aid the teenager, we must do what we can to help him answer these questions.

Much has already been done along the lines of giving sex education, but there is need to do far more. The question, "What is life all about anyway?" is a pretty tough one to answer. In my opinion, it is at this period of life that the challenge needs to be put to youth that he has an obligation to his race and to his culture which will not be fulfilled merely by passing on his biological heritage to his children. He must also contribute in some way, before he dies, to the culture which was his birthright. If he is to make his life worth while from the standpoint of society, he has an obligation to leave the world a better place for his children to live in, than it was at the beginning of his own life. Such an answer to the teenager's question, "What makes life worth while?" calls for responsibility and creative activity on his part.

The joys that come to the older years are usually involved, in one way or another, with the material, the social, and the spiritual welfare of mankind.

Such interests need to be kindled in youth, if they are to grow throughout the adult life. To a considerable degree, the answer to the "What makes life worth while?" question of the teenager will lay the course to be followed by him in the productive years of his life and on into the calmer years of his old age. Effective living, in the productive period, is in direct proportion to the degree of maturity arrived at by the individual—maturity in terms of ability of the mind to cope with problems faced by the individual—and to the resilience and vitality of his spirit. To be mature, one must find expression for the full range of one's talents. To get by is not enough. The fulfillment for which we all strive, consciously or unconsciously, in our life means doing our very best, the best that we are capable of.

The older years are the apex of life. They can be its crowning glory. It is true that our bodies begin to fail, but our minds keep on growing. As we strive to make our personal contribution to our children and our fellow man before we pass on, as we develop purpose in life, we will reach this crowning glory. Our lives will be worth while. We, as individuals, will live on, in the minds and hearts of those who follow us.

8. THE SIGNIFICANCE
   OF AGING

I've been anticipating this talk on the significance of aging.   Maybe, it's because my joints were a little creaky as I got out of bed this morning.

One of the things which has interested me about this subject is the fact that there is such confusion between the words "aging" and "aged."   All of us are inclined to think of aging through our own stereotyped idea of what aging is.   The usual stereotype is reflected in a delightful little poem which I would like to quote, in case you've not heard it.   It's called "Vanishing Youth," author unknown.   Here it is:

> How do I know that my youth is all spent?
> Well, my Get Up and Go has got up and went.
> But in spite of it all, I am able to grin,
> When I think where my Get Up and Go has been.

The terminal verse runs:

> Now since I've retired from life's competition
> I busy myself with complete repetition.
> I get up each morning and dust off my wits,
> Pick up the paper and read the "Obits."
> If my name is missing, I know I'm not dead,
> So I eat a good breakfast and go back to bed.

Amusing? Yes, yet this very stereotype in its broad acceptance by our people tends to stop us from making real progress on the so-called "national problems of aging." These problems have come in for some very critical examination recently, because of the White House Conference on Aging held in January 1961, and for other reasons.

Untapped resources of wisdom and maturity are available to our Nation, among the retired people. Persons no longer active in their careers but who have lived full lives, acquiring wisdom and maturity in the process, could participate beneficially, in many ways, in the community and the family life of the Nation. The stereotype that aging is a period when people are no longer useful and must be put on the shelf is blocking the logical solution of many of our problems—solutions which would benefit both society and the older persons themselves.

"Healthy maturity" is the phrase which I shall use to describe the state of older people about whom I am talking. A healthy maturity has certain assets in terms of the ability to do things and in terms of experience and wisdom; but, of course, it has some problems too.   People cannot grow old without having bodies that are weaker, and, therefore, they have more limitations within which they must live.

There are some preventive aspects of the aging phenomena.   If we live in certain ways, our bodies will age less rapidly.   I'm not advocating a "Fountain of Youth," such as Ponce de Leon searched for so **persistently, some centuries ago.   Death may be post**poned, but it cannot be eliminated.   We cannot have birth unless we have death.

Let us turn, now, to the meaning of the relationship between mind, body, and spirit, in terms of aging. What are the phenomena of aging?

As I see it, aging is a phenomenon of the physical body.   When energy is bound into organization as it most certainly is in the complex human body, it tries to escape.   This is in accordance with the second law of thermodynamics which tells us that energy always tries to seek its lowest energy level—like water running downhill toward the sea.   In much the same way, the aging process starts as soon as the fertilized ovum begins to multiply and to grow.   Energy in large quantities is routed into the growing body.   The energy tries to escape its confines.

As the life cycle progresses, more and more energy goes into restoring what is worn away by attrition. The body loses its resilience.   Fragility, brittleness, and rigidity are the order of the day.   Then, finally, the body as a topological structure breaks, which we have seen means death.

When there is purpose in life, when there is a reason for living, the physical energy available to the body is directed outward, largely, and the human organism is better able to maintain its integrity against the forces of attrition. Aging is a general phenomenon. It is applicable to all forms of life. It is also applicable to nonliving things. Molecules can age. Natural substances can age. Social groups can age. Nations can grow old. And, in time, mankind itself will age.

Actually, it seems to me that the phenomena of aging are intrinsic in the creation of any organization. In the early stages of organization, huge amounts of energy are routed into it so as to ensure its growth. But, as the organization grows and becomes older, as it becomes more mature, increasing amounts of energy are required just to bind it together. Eventually, in the process of time, all types of organizations break down. Energy which was used in building up the organization keeps on trying persistently to escape its confines, and in the end this will destroy any organization. Man is no exception.

Now, what is it that makes life worth living at the older ages? The answer to this question would appear to be that what makes life worth living at the older ages is pretty much the same thing as what makes it worth living at any age. However, the decrease of vigor and the hardening of tissues, the onset of brittle bones, the blunting of sensory acuity in sight and hearing, the surrendering of status upon retiring, the lessening of physical attractiveness, the menopause, the loss of friends, the loss of loved ones through death—these are some among the many, many factors requiring self-adjustment and reintegration of self on a modified, dynamic axis of interest.

If he is to overcome these kinds of handicaps, it is essential, therefore, that the older person have purpose in life. There are a number of major areas of concern to older people. Let us look at some of them.

Security is a vital necessity, because, as persons become older, they are more aware of their security requirements. They cannot feel secure in a rapidly changing environment. Traffic goes too fast. Noises are too disturbing. Lights are too glaring. Decisions called for are too taxing. For these various reasons, an older person needs a relatively safe community.

To make life worth while, fellowship also is required. Now, all persons are lonely when they are confined to their inner world of thought and feeling, and naturally all of us reach outward for contacts with others. The need to communicate, to love and **to be loved is a universal craving which must be satis-**fied. The older person, in particular, suffering from the shock of loss through death of cherished friends and loved ones, must fill this aching void.

He will find challenge and joy in community living, if it is designed so that he can participate in it. It will be a challenge for him to pass on to younger hands and minds and hearts what he has learned from life, and the cherished values of the race. To really live, he must somehow be a part of community life. He should have contact with children. He should mingle with families. Institutionalization, no matter how graciously conceived or tenderly administered, is a form of lifelessness before death. So fellowship for the older person is a must.

With advancing years, personal dignity is usually very rudely handled. It is a crushing blow, for instance, to lose the useful and respected role that one has enjoyed at younger ages. In general, the older person is still respected by his fellows, but it is for what he was and not for what he is. Yet, respect for **what one is, is the very foundation upon which personal** dignity rests. A person needs to feel that he is useful to those around him. And, personal dignity requires that one live in the present and for the future, not in the past. Dignity departs when one is tucked into a protective niche of inactivity until he dies.

The role of the older person in our society takes on a realistic place in the scheme of things only insofar as that person can become useful to his social order. The life cycle of man is very much like a relay race which each of us runs. Before we pass from the scene, we owe it to the human race to hand on the baton which we carry. We can take no pride in a race half run. If our life is worth the living, we will find our pride in having added something to the culture which was our birthright so that those who follow are at least a little better off than if we had not lived. This is our obligation to the race of man. The preserving and enhancing of our social and cultural birthrights are of paramount importance to the Nation and to the world. The pursuit of such an aim will automatically provide a useful and valued place for the older person in society. The lack of such an aim is one of the principal problems of aging in the world today.

Recognition of these circumstances could change the concept that aging is a problem for society into the concept that old age is a period of great value to society. Perhaps it is time to redefine our basic concept of retirement and make it a graduation point of departure into a period of service for social and cultural enhancement. The Nation can ill afford to waste its principal unused human resources. A healthy nation calls for renewed interest in science; for creative expression; for families and communities functioning at a high level of wellness; and for a rejuvenated awareness of our democratic ideals. For the nurture of these values, the qualified older person is ideally suited, both as guardian and as teacher. He can play a very special role in kindling in the minds and hearts of youth the flame of idealism.

9. THE TAPE RECORDINGS
OF HEREDITY

The other day, we discussed the life cycle, and during that talk we touched on the factor of heredity. Today, I would like to talk about the tape recordings of heredity.

Now, the life cycle of the individual starts with the fertilization of the ovum. The father and the mother contribute various qualities to the new individual, by sharing the chromosomes and genes which they have. As already mentioned, this transmission is built into a sort of codescript, a biological tape, as it were, which carries the building plans of the new individual—the instructions by which his body will be built.

I like the idea of tape recordings because of the attribute of high fidelity in tapes. It is rather amazing to me that a magnetic adjustment, such as takes place in the tape when a recording is made, can catch not only the voice sounds, but also many other qualities of the person. You can sense his moods. You know when he is tired. You know when he is under tension. Now, one of the qualities of tapes is the fact that once they have made their record, they will give back that record, time after time, with complete faithfulness.

The tape recordings of heredity are not magnetic. They are chemical. But, in many ways they are like the tapes—just as delicate, just as individualistic, just as sensitive, and just as rigid. Once we have our heritage, we're stuck with it!

I'm not a geneticist, and I do not intend to give a technical talk on genetics. Nor can I describe in detail the very fascinating advances being made in the biochemistry of inheritance. What I want to emphasize in this talk is really just one thing, and that is that heredity is a part of our animal nature. We are so inclined to think of the mental qualities of man and his spirit as something different from the animal kingdom, that we are prone to apply to heredity many of the things which simply aren't there. We say that Ann has her mother's blue eyes, and that Jim has the chin of his father; and, of course, that the disposition of Jim, which is rather mean, belongs to his father. Well, the first two things are heredity, all right; but the third factor is not. This is a part of something that's been brought about by the family or situation in which Jim lives.

The body has many defects. All of us have limitations. And, many of these are a part of the heritage of the person. Certain diseases which are not inherited do involve a structural weakness of the body which makes them more likely to occur if they have occurred previously in the family tree. For instance, the other day in an annual medical check-up, I was examined by a doctor who noticed that I had had a glaucoma condition in my eyes about ten years before. He asked me, "Have you discussed with your sons the hereditarial aspects of this?" I confessed that I hadn't. "Well," he said, "you really ought to, because glaucoma occurs much more frequently in those family trees which have had glaucoma in them. If the boys know this fact, then when they have any eye trouble at all, they can ask the doctor to look for early signs of glaucoma. It might, sooner or later, prevent blindness, because the condition was caught early."

The current interest in radiation and fallout has brought genetic questions to the fore. Last fall, for instance, I attended a seminar in Geneva which brought together geneticists, radiologists, and statisticians in connection with this subject. The threat of fallout has made the public quite conscious of the whole matter of mutations. It's difficult to go to a movie these days without having mutants spring out at you from the screen; and all sorts of wild imaginings are on the loose with reference to what mutations are and what their significance will be in our lives.

What kind of information on mutations is it that the geneticist is after for health purposes? What are mutations anyway? What kinds of deficiencies are preponderantly due to genetic factors? What kinds of malformations? What kinds of diseases? Are fetal and infant death rates a part of the genetic picture?

Well, there are all kinds of questions and speculations. Some of them deal directly with our interest here in high-level wellness. For instance, is the geneticist interested in the weakness or the durability of the body as an organized whole? How much interest does he have in the whole matter of human behavior relative to survival? To what degree is he interested in the inbreeding of the human stock? What is the relative significance of offspring from close relatives, with respect to mutations?

Sir Julian Huxley points out that natural selection converts accident into apparent design and randomness into organized patterns. But mutation merely provides the raw material of evolution. It is a random affair. It takes place in all directions. Genes are giant molecules, and their mutations are the result of slight alterations in their structure. Some of these alterations are truly chance arrangements, as uncaused, or at least as unpredictable, as the jumping of an electron from one orbit to another inside of an atom. Others are the result of the impact of some external agency, like X-rays, or ultraviolet radiation, or fallout; and, as Sir Julian puts it nicely, in his book *Evolution in Action:*

> "Natural selection operates through imperfection. Mutation, we may say, is an imperfection in the basic property of living substance, of reproducing itself unaltered; but without it there could have been no change, and so no improvement of any sort. The wastage of lives in each generation is an imperfection in the process of living; but without it there could have been no differential survival, and so no further biological improvement. Imperfection is the necessary basis for selection, and so for any possible perfection. . . . natural selection converts randomness into direction, and blind chance into apparent purpose."[4]

In another of his writings, *Man in the Modern World,* Sir Julian poses the basic issue of heredity in the culture. He says:

> ". . . in civilized human communities of our present type, the elimination of defect by natural selection is largely (though of course by no means wholly) rendered inoperative by medicine, charity, and the social services; while, as we have seen, there is no selection encouraging favorable variations. The net result is that many deleterious mutations can and do survive, and the tendency to degradation of the germ-plasm can manifest itself. . . . We must be able to pick out the genetically inferior stocks with more certainty, and we must set in motion

> counter-forces making for faster reproduction of superior stocks, if we are to reverse or even arrest the trend. And neither of these, as we have seen, is possible without an alteration of social system."[5]

The genetic dilemma which we face poses problems to deep-held beliefs, in health, medicine, and religion. For instance, we consider the saving of life a mandate. It takes precedence over all other elements. The right to die, the right to live, the right to pass on life to others—what should be our attitude toward questions such as these, if we pick up the gauntlet tossed by Sir Julian?

Of one thing we can be sure. The power to reproduce has in it the necessity of death. The potential immortality of the race requires the mortality of the individual. Reproduction and immortality are incompatible.

Of another thing we can be certain: nature is prodigal with life. It is difficult for those of us who have been reared in the Western culture to think of life as cheap, because we have been taught to think that it is precious. Yet, with all parents, the wastage of sperm and ovum resources—so-called "fertility wastage" — involves astronomical numbers. Almost any one of the particular blendings between a particular ovum and a particular sperm could have resulted in an individualistic boy or girl, just as precious as the particular ones actually born. But if potential life were as priceless as individual life is deemed to be, then the "might-have-beens," the never-to-be persons who could have lived, outnumber those who do live and die, as do the sands of the sea outnumber the persons standing on its shore.

The universal "natural law" to which all forms of life must conform is that excess fertility is essential for the survival of the species. Man is no exception. But if man, through the medical and health sciences limits his mortality, he must likewise limit his fertility, so as to bring births and deaths into balance. Without counterbalancing controls on births, overpopulation will engulf the human culture of free man.

Natural selection holds several lessons for man. Though there are still barriers against so-called race-crossing, the whole human race has become increasingly a single interbreeding unit instead of an increasing number of noninterbreeding units. Evolution is progressing for mankind as a whole. In particular, the mind of man is in evolution. It is an emergent mind. Natural selection also tells us that the human personality, the person considered as a whole, is of primary importance. Hence, our civilization must find its progress through the cooperation of integrated individual personalities.

To achieve the future envisaged by man requires a sound biological heritage for man. We need to become interested in the heredity which we pass on to our children. Whether it is good or bad, this will be their starting point. Upon it, they will have to build. The mind of man and the culture of man and, ultimately, the very destiny of man will depend upon his biological heritage.

10. SOCIAL CHANGE AND THE CHANGING LIFE CYCLE

In the talk today, I would like to consider social change and the changing life cycle.

We all know that there are many more old people than there used to be; that is, they are a higher proportion of the total population. Most of us do not know why this is so, nor do we realize the magnitude of the change. The change comes about due to the fact that the life cycle is longer, on the average. The average duration of life has been greatly extended due to the many supporting measures introduced into daily living. These have tended to make the physical environment more favorable for the preservation of life, that is, human life. The means of bringing about the increase in longevity have included: the enhanced effectiveness of medical care; the great advances in sanitation, such as those concerned with pure food and water, disposal of wastes, and the like;

and the advances in food production and material goods available to the consumer.

The extraordinary change in the length of the life cycle is probably best seen if we can think in terms of what the statistician calls "cohorts." By cohort, he means a group of people born at the same time. Now, when you consider a hundred thousand males or a hundred thousand females born in 1890 and compare them with a hundred thousand males or females born in 1950, you can see, in examining the way they die off, the enormous increase in older people. In rough terms, slightly over one-quarter of the men and one-third of the women of 1890 will survive to the age of 75; whereas, in the cohort of 1950, well over one-half of the men and almost three-quarters of the women can be expected to survive to this age. And, consider this fact. Only three-fourths of the females born in 1890 survived to the age of 10 years; whereas, three-fourths of the cohort of females born in 1950 will live to be 73 years of age. The implications of these facts are staggering.

The older years are no longer the prerogative of a few of us in these United States, but are years which will be lived by the large majority of all of us. When we ask ourselves why the life cycle has changed so vastly, we come up against the realization that we are living in a revolutionary world. By revolutionary, I do not mean from a political standpoint, although it is certainly true that a good deal of that is going on, too. I mean a revolutionary world from the standpoint of man's struggles against the natural environment, his attempts to make the natural environment more favorable for his survival and for his comfort.

Now, the first revolution of this nature was probably the agricultural revolution. Man found a way to raise his food substances, and, in doing this, he freed himself from the vagaries of the physical environment, especially climate, so that he wouldn't go hungry or starve to death. Several hundred years ago, the industrial revolution came along, and this made it possible for him to make in abundance the goods which he needed for his purposes. About the same time, he learned about germs, and, with this knowledge, he was able, through sanitation, pure water, and the like, to make a much healthier environment, so that people began to live longer. As the population began to grow, man pushed out in every direction. This brought with it the revolution of transportation and the revolution of communication.

These revolutions are still going on today. Agriculture, for instance, has learned how to increase grain yields and quality enormously, through hybridization. It has also learned how to protect crops against insect life. And, it has used the science of genetics to enhance the value of its livestock; as, for example, the yield of milk per cow and the percentage of butterfat in the milk.

Industry is now going through an additional revolution—automation, which is using the new electronics to make industrial production automatic. Nobody knows, yet, where this will end. And, transportation is reaching the jet age and the rocket age, and we don't know where that is going either.

Possibly the greatest revolution of all is taking place in the ability of man to wage war. War potentialities have become too deadly to contemplate. The destructive power of the atom, bacteriological warfare, and other agents which science has made available is such that, if used in full-scale war in the future, there is every likelihood that the whole human race will be eliminated.

Now, it is perfectly obvious as one examines these various revolutions that the thing behind them all is what we call science. Through science, we are replacing the natural environment by a man-made environment which we can control. Even though it looks like we aren't doing a very good job now of controlling it, it is controllable. The difficulty lies in the way we go about it.

Let us now summarize the major social changes which have taken place within our lifetime. It is a shrinking world. It is a crowded world. It is a world striving for higher standards of living. And, it is an older world. Furthermore, the very fact that it is getting more and more crowded, and that we are living more and more in cities means that it is a world of mounting tensions. The whole ecology—

that is, the interrelation of life forms and their environment—throughout the world is shifting, due to the population growth and the spread of urbanization. The impact of population increase and of the spreading culture of man upon other life forms is but poorly appreciated as yet.   Dr. R. A. Piddington, in his book *The Limits of Mankind*, brings this out very nicely.   He says that certain major life forms are disappearing from the world, and, as he puts it, "the noxious bacteria and the viruses have enormously profited from the abundance of human material which, crudely speaking, lessens the distance that they must travel between one meal and the next."[6]

These material advances which have been made mean that it is a world of changing value attributes. We are increasingly materialistic.   And there has been a shift from positive to negative aims.   By and large, the people of the United States are no longer fighting *for* something—unless one regards fighting to keep the status quo as fighting for something.   On the whole, we like our lot in life and feel reasonably secure in it.   Consequently, our normal reaction to threatening situations tends to take the form of being *against* almost anything which promises to disturb our peace of mind or upset our favored position in the world.   This means that the stimulus of being dynamically *for* something, something positive, some cause or goal, is missing from our lives, and that, consequently, we have a lessening of the creative activities of which we are capable.

I'd like to call to your attention the fact that, while science is behind some of these social changes, it isn't the basic thing that's behind our changing values or our outlook on life. Our shift in values and our negative outlook on life represents something that's mental, something that's psychological. Science is a technique of the mind, and, consequently, the real revolution is one of the mind. Actually, what we have done is to free the creative imagination of man to work at full potential in connection with the development of the natural sciences. Unfortunately, with references to almost everything else—that is, almost every other field—we still impose a good many barriers around the use of the creative imagination. This largely accounts for the fact that science is growing by leaps and bounds while social change falters by the way.

Most of us wish that the world wouldn't move quite so fast or quite so dangerously. Yet, stability will never again be static. How in the world can we achieve stability when the creative imagination is on the loose? As I see it, the thing that underlies the whole revolutionary transition through which man is going is the fact that his mind is evolving, and we probably will not get stability unless we can arrive at a stage of its evolution which allows stability in a dynamic sense. For a good many years, scientists considered the whole matter of energy as static, but it took an Einstein to see that the whole thing is relative; it just does not have any meaning unless even light itself is considered in a relative way. Well, I think the whole process of the mind is relative. Stability *is* possible, but it must be a dynamic type of stability.

Man's future rests upon the evolution of the mind in such a way that it can function as a mechanism dealing with problems in a relative way. We need not fear change. We should welcome the whole matter of social change, the changing life cycle, and the evolution of the mind of man. All we need to do is to extend the relativity theory to the mind of man, and we'll get along very nicely.

11. THE EMERGENT MIND

The next few talks in this series will be on various aspects of the mind. The one today is called "The Emergent Mind." In it, I shall consider three questions: What is the mind of man? How has it evolved? Where is it going?

Let us look at the first of these. What is the mind anyway? Does a worm have a mind? Does an insect have a mind? Does a dog or a horse have a mind? Did primitive man have a mind? The newborn baby—has it a mind?

Well, personally, I'm inclined to go along with Julian Huxley on this. He says there is really no such thing as a mind, in its own right. He holds that a mind is not an entity, a separate thing which inhabits our skulls. It is, rather, a complex of activities performed by the brain and the body.

Several components go into the mind. The brain—at least a part of it—serves as a very complicated telephone exchange. It handles incoming and outgoing calls. In the memory cells of the brain are stored a vast library of facts and information. This library stretches on into dim recesses—we might call them the archives—within which the subconscious mind resides and from there on into a museum where facts about the race are stored, a sort of racial type of memory.

In the mind, there's also a court of justice for decision, and a seat of government for the body as a whole. As Lewis Mumford puts it:

> "By transferring authority to a controlling intelligence, sensitized by feeling, and enlarged by imagination, man sometimes endangered his personal survival, but he opened the possibility of further development." [7]

Now, the significance of information varies according to who receives it. Let us take, for example, the light from a bright star, as seen by a man and his dog. In each instance, a bright point of light is seen. Perhaps the dog sees this more clearly than the man. However, the interpretation of what that star is differs considerably, according to the dog's mind and the man's mind. To the dog, it very probably is just a point of light. The man, however, knows that it is another sun, more or less like the sun in our own solar system, but much farther away. Yet, only a few hundred years ago, the man would have considered this point of light more or less like the dog now considers it. Of one thing we can be sure, our mind is in a process of emergent understanding.

The mind is a very complex thing to define, but I would like to try a definition of it.   My definition would be that it is the ability-complex of man which enables him to use his inner world for the purpose of solving the problems of everyday living.   That sounds rather simple, doesn't it? Let's enlarge on it. Man takes the sum total of the information which comes to him through his sense organs from the outer world; stores, integrates, and tries it out by various experiences; modifies and continually reorganizes it as information available to him from his inner world.   The total complex resulting from this process is the mind.

The mind grows, just as the body grows.   And, since the primary function of the mind is to solve problems, our ability to solve problems also grows.

Now, the second question: How has the mind evolved?   How has it emerged from its biological base?   We know that irritability is a fundamental characteristic of protoplasm.   This characteristic is a part of the chemical structure of the cells.   In the course of natural evolution, cells became specialized. Certain cells became specialized in the quality of sensitivity.   Consequently, we have in man the five basic senses that are identifiable: sight, hearing, taste, smell, and touch.   These are our windows to the outside world.

Vision, of course, is the sense that has the greatest depth.   It penetrates the farthest.   We depend greatly on sight. Hearing is one of the most interesting of the senses. You can hear around corners. Sound waves don't have to travel in straight lines, as light waves do. You can hear in the dark. Bats can pick a mosquito out of the air on the darkest night simply by the echo of sound waves which come back to them—a sort of radar mechanism which is probably much more efficient than any radar that man has been able to develop, so far. Likewise, the porpoise in the sea uses sound to find his way around, and can negotiate in the darkest night quite as well as a man can in the light of day.

We are inclined to downgrade the senses of touch, smell, taste, and hearing, and depend mostly upon sight. There are instances on record, however, in which human beings who do not have sight have been able to develop these other senses to an extraordinary degree. Take the case of one young man I heard about who had lost his sight at the age of three. Instead of accepting this as a deterrent to leading a full life, he decided that he was going to be a normal person in an active, adult world. Over a period of years, he developed his hearing and his other senses to such a degree that he is now able to walk about the streets of a busy city without either cane or seeing-eye dog. It is not just a question of memory, because he can do this in a city that he has never been in before.

Some animals have sense organs that are more sensitive than those of man. Take the bloodhound, for instance. He can follow a trail which is many hours old. The eagle can see to great distances. Bats can find their way around by means of ultrasonic vibrations which cannot be detected by the human ear. Bees use the ultraviolet spectrum, something that we humans can't distinguish. Furthermore, they have some very special apparatus that we know but little about yet, by means of which they can sense polarized forms of light.

The limitations on the acuity of the senses of man are not real limitations to his mental development. With his mind, he is able to develop machinery which will extend his senses. So far as we know, radio waves cannot as yet be sensed by any animal, yet man turns on his radio and hears them as a part of his daily life.

From these various considerations, we come to the conclusion that, while sensitiveness is something man shares with all forms of life, his ability to use his mind to solve problems is far superior to that of any other form of life.

Our third question was: Where is the mind of man going; how will it develop from here on? At present, it is dealing primarily with conceptual thought. Let me illustrate, by a story concerning Helen Keller, what conceptual thought is. When Miss Keller was very young, she became blind and deaf and dumb. Her teacher, trying to reestablish communication between the child and the outside world, had Helen hold one hand in a pan of water and with the other one write the word "w-a-t-e-r." Suddenly, Helen's face lighted up, and she communicated, "Why, all things have names." Well, this became a concept at that moment. And, concepts such as this one open the door of the mind of man to an expanding future. Names, abstracts, and the use of symbols to describe these abstracts have led man to systems of logic. Through these, he has developed logical systems of thought, such as mathematics, science, philosophy, and religion. In the early stages of these logical systems, he kept them quite separate; but, to an ever-increasing degree, we are seeing that all of them are interrelated. And, interrelatedness is leading us to a higher form of consciousness.

What is consciousness? Well, I don't know the answer. You will recall that, in our talk on energy, I said that one of the great mysteries of the universe is energy and another is consciousness. It is my view, however, that the conceptual mind of man is evolving into an intuitional type of mind—a mind that is very definitely able to interrelate things better.

My answer, therefore, to the question, "Where is the mind of man going?" is that I don't know. But, of this I am pretty sure, it is evolving into something very much more complex and very much more interrelated. In our mind of the future, we will be able to solve our problems in an interrelated way.

12. THE PROBLEM-SOLVING MECHANISM

Today, I would like to discuss the problem-solving mechanism of man. You will recall that in the last talk, on the emergent mind, I raised three questions: What is the mind of man? How has it evolved? Where is it going?

In considering what is the mind of man, we defined it as: the ability-complex of man which enables him to use his inner world for the purpose of solving the problems of everyday living. As we discuss today this problem-solving mechanism, we shall focus on three new questions: First, "How does the mind work?" Second, "What are its principal components or parts?" And third, "How can the mind be kept in good working order?"

As to the first question—"How does the mind work?"—let me admit right off that I don't know the answer. And, I venture to say that few persons would claim to know it. Various of the scientific disciplines are contributing to our knowledge of the *brain,* and how it works. The anatomist can tell us a great deal about the structure of the brain and of the various nuclei contained within it, the way the fibers run, and things of this order. The biochemist has knowledge of some of the chemical changes that go on in the functioning brain cells. The physiologist, by means of experimentation, has discovered which parts of the brain do what. The biophysicist is delving into the matter of electrical brain waves, as the brain functions on different types of problems. The psychologist, the behavioral specialist, and the psychiatrist are digging down into the subterranean passageways of the brain, trying to fathom why certain things occur under certain circumstances. And, the doctors and the clergy are trying to relate the actions of people to the way their mental processes work.

It is only very recently that a new science has emerged which is trying to look at the operations of the brain as a whole. It is called cybernetics. This new science probably has its origin in the great amount of knowledge now being obtained by men through the operation of the digital computers, the so-called "giant brains." And, as technicians delve into the processes of mechanical systems of calculation and problem-solving, there are so many parallels emerging between these mechanical systems and the way the brain works that substantial progress is being made toward understanding how the mind works. However, we still have a long way to go! Regardless of how far science ultimately goes in this direction, it is doubtful if a mechanical way to "know thyself" will ever be devised by science. It seems likely that this will continue to reside with the individual.

Even though we do not know how the mind works, we can understand a great deal about its working ability. I do not know how my watch works, and yet I know how to take care of my watch. I know a great deal about the various parts that go to make it up. I know something about the stem and how to wind it. I know when the mainspring is broken. I can see a smashed crystal and know how to go about replacing it. All of these are real things, which sufficient understanding enables us to take proper care of. In the same way, I can understand enough about my mind, enough about its parts to enable me to do a pretty good job of caring for it and keeping it in good repair.

Now to the second question: What are the principal components or parts of the problem-solving mechanism? There are many, but I have eight identified which I would like to discuss. Each one is of sufficient importance to merit special consideration as a separate talk. They will therefore be the themes for the next eight talks in this series.

To see the broad panorama of these components of problem-solving, I shall enumerate them briefly, here.

First of all, there is *communication*. Obviously, we cannot solve problems unless we have the relevant data or information upon which our minds can work. Therefore, communication through the sensory inlets and outlets is all-important.

The second element is the *storage* of information or knowledge. We think of this in terms of memory, proper; but man has also extended the limits of his memory to all parts of his body, and to all reaches of his culture. The resources of the libraries of the world and the accumulated knowledge of humanity are potentially available to the mind in solving its problems.

The third component of the problem-solving mechanism is *values*. We cannot make judgments which are needed in the solution of problems unless we have a scale of values. Hence, the values that are ours, that we are reared with, that we have made our own, are all-important in connection with the problem-solving mechanism.

The fourth element is *imagination*. This might surprise you, because most of us think of it as a rather intangible sort of thing. However, imagination has its roots in the biological phenomenon of fantasy, common to all of us, arising because electrical impulses can flow broadly over the cortical cells of the brain. In man, imagination has taken this phenomenon and structured it purposefully, making it possible for man to *postulate solutions of problems*—an all-important component of the problem-solving mechanism.

With the aid of imagination, man was able to make his next step forward in problem-solving—that is, the separation of his self, his inner world, from all of the outer world about him. This *concept of self* has allowed man to set up criteria as to what is good for him and what is not, and has thus equipped him with the means of making decisions.

The sixth component of the mind is described as *balance* or *integration* of self. We are quite aware of the importance of a balance wheel in the operation of a watch. Well, the mind needs one, too. That is, when it is solving problems, it needs to solve them from a point of balance, a point at which there is equilibrium with reference to all of the knowledge and information available to it.

Obviously, even if all the components which have been discussed are present and effective, they still must work together as a whole. Hence, *maturity in wholeness* becomes, itself, a seventh component.

The final component of the problem-solving mechanism, one which is very important to the emergent mind, is *purpose*. To an ever-increasing degree, in the pursuit of purpose we find the courage to venture broadly, so often necessary in solving complex problems which cross interdisciplinary lines. Systems formation of knowledge in depth invariably requires the broadening of perspective.

Now, we come to the third and final question: How can the mind be kept in good working order? Well, how can a watch be kept in good working order? First of all, by not mistreating it. We don't drop our watch into water or let it fall to the pavement if we can help it. We try to guard it against the kinds of things that will damage it. Then periodically we have it cleaned and oiled. This we know is necessary for a watch if it's to keep good time. Also, this reduces the wear and tear that would otherwise eventually break it down. And finally, when it does break down for one reason or another—when we smash the crystal or wind the stem too tight—we have our watch repaired. We repair it because we know it has a lot of service in it, if it has not been badly abused. Well, these are the same kinds of things that we need to do in connection with the care of our minds as problem-solving mechanisms.

In the course of developing the talks to follow on these eight major components, I expect, as a part of each, to consider how we can maintain in good working order the particular part of the mind under discussion.

The care and nurture of the mind is not a job for your doctor or your clergyman. The responsibility of keeping this priceless problem-solving mechanism in good working order rests squarely on one person—you!

Now, we know that there are watches which are good and watches which are poor. We know that some of them are highly jeweled, and others are without jewel movement. Generally speaking, the ones that are less delicately made and less delicately balanced are easier to take care of, but they don't do quite as good a job. The really fine watches need special care.

It is the same way with the mind. Some minds are better than others. The really fine minds must be given better opportunity to emerge and to perform at the high level of which they are capable. While this is in part a job for the individual, it must also become a greater concern for society.

The problems of society are man-made. Man has within himself the mechanism to solve these problems.

13. COMMUNICATION

This talk is on communication. In my last talk, I dealt with the mind as a problem-solving mechanism, and cited a number of components or parts which make up this problem-solving mechanism. The first of these is communication.

In no way is the human mind so like the "great brains" or giant digital computers of our times as it is with respect to communication channels or pathways. No matter how perfect a digital computer may be or how elaborate its memory mechanism, it cannot do its job unless it has access to the data needed for the solution of the problem which it is tackling. The data must not only be correct, they must also be complete. Furthermore, they must not be distorted. To the degree that the data are not available to the digital computer or that they are distorted, the computer will come up with wrong answers. So it is, also, with the human mind.

Now, I have complete faith in the human mind as a problem-solving mechanism. It is my belief that most human beings start life with a reasonably good problem-solving mechanism, but communication channels are vulnerable. Even the most magnificent mind in the world could be made completely impotent if the channels of information were too badly clogged. Probably the greatest crime of social man against biological man is his frequent attempts to constrict the channels of communication so that the human mind cannot do its job. In an attempt to control social structure, social man frequently and deliberately distorts facts. He controls sources of data that should be left open, and thus he makes it almost impossible for the mind to do its work.

Sometimes, social man tries to close down the channels inside the mind as well as outside. He does this by implanting in the mind and the muscles of the body numerous fixations which make it difficult for the mind to be able to solve problems in a logical way. Such fixations act like rusty wires, and set up resistance to the passing currents which should move freely.

The stages of communication are three in number—input, output, and the integration of stored information. We must be able to use our sense organs so as to perceive the incoming signals. We must likewise be able to transmit and express the information that we wish to pass out. In the electronic computers, we call these particular functions "input" and "output." In addition to input and output in the human system, we have a vast amount of information within our bodies which must be organized, sifted, and developed into a synthetic whole. In other words, the information needed by the growing body is of two types—that which comes from the outside world through sensory organs, and that which is stored, assembled, transmitted, and constantly re-integrated and used, as inside information.

In early childhood, particularly, the mind is like an open sponge. Outside information is of primary importance to its growth. In order to learn, the child must believe. In the early years he accepts as true what he is taught (unless the "facts" are labeled either as fantasy or as untruths). This is the basic reason why it is so important for the child to be able to trust his parents implicitly. Trust in his parents is his bastion of security. This he must have in order to be able to learn and to adventure into the rapidly expanding circle of the outer world.

As I have mentioned previously, the sense organs open up gradually and progressively over the growth period. Jurgen Ruesch describes well the phenomenal way in which the motor system develops after birth. The lips, the tongue, the eyes, the neck and shoulder muscles, the arms, the hands, the fingers, the legs, the feet—all develop their respective motor functions. Although hand and mouth and hand and eye coordination begin to appear rather early, these movements do not become smooth and poised until approximately the age of 8 or 10.

Let me given you Ruesch's chronological time scale of the development of communication: During the intra-uterine period, the fetus responds to thermal, mechanical, and chemical stimuli. In the neo-natal period, the first 12 weeks of life, the infant learns to respond to tactile, auditory, and visual stimuli. In babyhood, from 3 to about 24 months, mastery of the head, the eye, and hand movements appears, and then in rapid succession those of the trunk, the fingers, the legs, and the feet. The second year of life brings speech to the child. During the infancy period, from 2 to 5 years, interpersonal communication is established with one person at a time—the mother, the father, brother or sister, and perhaps a relative living in the household. In later childhood, from 6 to 12 years, group communication comes about, especially through contacts in the school. And, during adolescence and the teens, interpersonal communication and the techniques of living and operating within groups are learned. Adulthood, of course, brings the peak of communication. As the older ages come on, the sensory openings begin to close, and communication becomes steadily more difficult for the individual.

It is important to realize that the closing down of the sense organs with the aging process is not necessarily a catastrophic factor. All sorts of mechanisms have been developed to extend the sensitivity of hearing, sight, and the other senses. For instance, I've been particularly interested recently in the work of Frank Arthur Geldard who describes certain neglected possibilities of communication. He asks the questions: What is it possible for the skin to do? Can we develop a cutaneous language which might prove to be a perfectly satisfactory means of communication? He begins by examining the dimension of mechanical vibration, in particular, locus, intensity, duration, and frequency. All of these elements, in terms of mechanical vibration, hold out distinct language possibilities. He developed a simple alphabetical code, and, after only 35 hours of training, he found that an individual could receive sentences through the skin with 90 percent accuracy when these were transmitted at a rate of 38 five-letter words per minute.

Isn't this fantastic? It shows that we have not begun to tap the surface of the possibilities of cutaneous sensation as a mechanism for communication.

Geldard points out that there are many phenomena other than the simple mechanical vibrations which it might be possible to develop, such as volume, pitch, and the like.

Let us now examine the similarities between the great brains or computers and the human brain. Basically, there are two types of electronic computers—the so-called "great brains." One of these is called the digital computer; and the other, the analogue computer. It is important to distinguish the difference between "digital" codification and "analogic" codification of language. Digital refers to discrete facts, discrete words; while analogue involves movement through time and the interrelatedness of concepts. The use of words, therefore, has more or less the same types of limitations as the digital computer. These limitations are involved with "yes" and "no" answers. They're involved with black and white. There is no place for a "gray zone" of reaction.

Nonverbal communication, however—the movement of hands, facial features, and body in order to express the thoughts of a person—is analogic in character. You can all recall certain persons who use their hands and feet and bodies when they talk, and who are almost unable to express themselves without these types of nonverbal emphasis. All of us do this to a certain degree. We think of a person as deadpan, who uses no such muscular expressions to supplement his words.

At the hotel one evening, when I was dining with a couple, I remarked that there was a lady at the adjoining table who had a little spider on her dress. "I was on the point of crushing it with my hand," I said, "when I observed that it was a little jeweled spider." We were laughing about what might have happened, if I had whacked her, and were considering what I should have done. The lady at the table said, "You should have done this, not that." The "this" was a movement of her finger to flip the spider off; and the "that" was a movement of her hand, dealing a crushing blow. Without doubt, such nonverbal movements communicated better than could have been accomplished by words alone.

Maintenance of open channels of communication and access to data is vital, if the mind is to serve satisfactorily its function as a problem-solving mechanism. There is no alternative. Open channels of communication are more important to the freedom of the mind than any other component of the problem-solving mechanism.

High-level wellness, both for the individual and for society, cannot be maintained unless the lines of communication are kept open and access to needed data guaranteed. We cannot have well individuals or a well society with closed channels of communication. Individuals and societies must be free to pick and choose solutions. A free mind can adventure. A free mind is a healthy mind. Maintenance of the freedoms to which we are dedicated both as individuals and as a society depends more directly upon open channels of communication than upon any other single factor.

14. STORAGE OF KNOWLEDGE AND EXPERIENCE

This is a talk on "Storage of Knowledge and Experience," in the High-Level Wellness Series.

As outlined in an earlier talk, storage of data is the second component of the problem-solving mechanism which we call the mind. We will take up, first, the types of memory stored in body tissues. Following this, we will consider the question of how the mind organizes these sources of data so that it can use them. And finally, we will discuss how to keep this component of the problem-solving mechanism in good working order.

There are three types of memory in the body tissues. The first and most important is that of the nervous system. This is where we store knowledge. The second is the muscular system, in which we largely store our experience in life, and which has a great deal to do with the memories that we call emotions. The third place where memories are

stored is the body cells. Here, we take care of the
chemical memories so important to the body.

Let's start with the nervous system. At the beginning of life, it is more or less like an empty book, or
perhaps we should say an empty tape since we are
now accustomed to tape recordings. There must be
thousands of miles of this empty tape in the human
cortex, just waiting their turn to have knowledge
inscribed upon them. In the human brain alone,
there are approximately 10 billion cortical cells.
This is an enormous number, and they are arranged
in action areas, subdivided in turn into various
regions and functions.

I have been particularly interested in the work of
Dr. Wilder Penfield, who has discovered in the tem-
poral cortex of the brain a so-called interpretive
cortex where a stream of consciousness in the human
brain can be electrically reactivated. Contained in
this record are all those things of which the individual was once aware, in such detail as a man might
hope to remember for a few seconds or minutes,
perhaps, but which are lost to voluntary recall after
that time. As Penfield puts it:

> "Transient electrical potentials move . . .
> through the circuits of the nervous system, leav-
> ing a path that can be followed again. The
> pattern of this pathway, from neuron to neuron,
> along each nerve-cell body and fiber and junc-
> tion, is the recorded pattern of each man's
> past."[8]

So far as I know, no one is yet sure exactly how the recordings are made. It is probably, however, a chemical type of recording, brought about by the rearrangement of the molecules in some way.

Let us now look at muscle memory. It is customary for us to consider the biological basis of the mind as relegated more or less exclusively to the brain and the central nervous system. Now, it is true that data, in the form of facts and information and beliefs, are absorbed through the various senses into the nervous system, and tucked away in the memory depositories of the brain. But, it seems to me quite reasonable to postulate that experience, in the form of muscular response to such data, is stored very largely in the form of tension patterns in the muscle fibers themselves.

If this is true, it would mean that the biological basis for the mind resides largely in the memory potential of an interrelated neuromuscular complex, and that the processes of learning are frequently involved with teaching the muscles how to walk, and talk, and carry on coordinated muscular activity. It would further mean that, while the memory of the actual experience is stored as tension patterns in the muscle fibers, the memory of how this coordination was brought about is stored as a pattern in the brain.

It has been demonstrated in the laboratory that a minimum suggestion of previous situations, coming into the mind through perception, is quite sufficient to recall and to reexperience situations deeply buried in the subconscious. Thus, the emotions aroused by fear, hate, prejudice, and the frustrations of years ago are reactivated many times in adult life, and in almost their original intensity. Many of the tensions from which we are suffering in our present-day life probably have their origin in unresolved emotional experiences which lie buried as coordinated neuro-muscular memories, and which can be triggered off and reexperienced time after time. This undoubtedly results in a total impact of tension on the tissues of the body out of all proportion to that of the original experience.

The lie detector tests, for instance, which we have seen dramatized in television and in the movies, are another example of how such muscle tension patterns get out of control and betray the individual in spite of himself.

The third type of memory is that of the body cells, which is chemical in type. Perhaps an illustration is in order. About ten years ago, in an attempt to control an incipient glaucoma—a condition of high fluid pressure in one of my eyes—the doctor kept putting different kinds of medicine into the eye so as to keep the pressure down. This went on for two or three years. Finally, the skin around the eye became so allergic to one after another of these medicines that in the end I was unable to use any of them. That was ten years ago, but the skin cells still rebel against any sort of medical eye drops. That shows how stubborn a chemical memory can be.

How does the mind organize these sources of data into a whole, so that they can be used for practical, everyday problem-solving purposes? Science has discovered recently that there are electrical waves which seem to scan the cortical cells of the brain all the time. There are several types of these waves. The most consistent is the so-called alpha rhythm, with a frequency of somewhere around 8 to 13 cycles per second. It appears to be constantly searching for pictures. It would seem that the alpha rhythm is associated with the formation of ideas; hence its continual search for analogous situations or images.

The fastest of the known brain rhythms is the beta rhythm, which has a frequency cycle of about 14 to 30 per second. This is found in conditions of nervous tension, whether acute, or prolonged, or in actual anxiety states. The theta rhythm, with a cycle of 4 to 7 vibrations per second, appears to be continuously searching for pleasure and for pleasant sensations. When these are found, it ceases its restless march; and when the pleasure ceases, it once more continues to search.

As already indicated, pain, fear, and emotional distress can become locked into tissues and constitute a never-ending source of increasing tension within the human structure. Locked-in pain not only can raise tension, but it can also prevent the healing of tissues.

There has been very little experimentation along these lines, but I'm inclined to think that we could shorten hospital stays materially if we ran the pain out of tissues promptly after having severe traumatic experiences.

The same is undoubtedly true of emotional pain. The death of a loved one, for instance, should not be kept inside of one's self and brooded over; it should be discussed with others, and eventually the pain in the tissues can be relieved by this process.

The mind, apparently, can cope with almost anything, if it can just get at the available data. I like to think of reality as an axis of awareness around which we organize our thought pattern and to which we gear all of the data resources available in the various memory depositories of the body. It is a dynamic balance of an integrated self which is maintained as a moving axis of equilibrium between the various influences which affect the individual, both from within and without.

Now, let us turn to the preventive measures for maintaining this storage component of the problem-solving mechanism in good working order. Primarily, the task is to maintain access to data—access to all of the data which we have available within our body structure. Since our mind cannot do a good job when it comes to blocked pathways, we must clear these pathways of the knots of pain and fear which are buried in our tissues. This is a job which might, at times, call for the help of a psychiatrist. However, since much of the vague fears and anxieties start very early in life, I think we should experiment with the pre-school child, to relieve his mind of many of these anchor points for later neuroses.

Another thing that we could do is to systematically run out recent pain, whether it is physical or emotional, in the first 24 to 48 hours after the experience occurs. This is relatively simple to do, and the individual can be taught how to do it himself. Basically, it involves reliving the situation, step by step, until the pain is experienced in its original intensity. After a varying number of times of reexperiencing the painful situation, the pain leaves the tissues and the person is cleared from the necessity of coping with it later as a hidden knot of pain.

Of course, there are obstacles in the way of facing up to reality. Many things in our social and cultural practices, for example, tend to symbolize and ritualize fixed beliefs, and thus to erect around them a wall of habit—or, as we would term it in this talk, a wall of "muscular memory." Since anything repeated many times involves the use of muscles, and muscle memories do not change as easily as do the memories in the nervous system, it becomes heresy to challenge concepts held in the minds of others who cherish them. This is undoubtedly responsible for part of the blockage which impedes the problem-solving mechanism.

In summary, let me say that the most important single ingredient of a well mind is its ability to continually reintegrate the sum total of its stored knowledge and experience. This ability depends on:

1. Willingness to face inconsistencies in our thinking.
2. Willingness to reexamine beliefs or practices in the light of contradictions which come to our attention.
3. Willingness to readjust such beliefs or practices into an integrated and consistent whole, at some new level of adjustment and harmony.

Remember, a well mind is an open mind! Facing reality, in the light of *all* the available data, is an essential if the problem-solving mechanism is to do its job well.

15. VALUES AND
   VALUE JUDGMENTS

This talk will deal with values and value judgments.

A scale of values is an essential component of the problem-solving function of the mind. By means of the imagination, we set up various postulates in connection with particular problems and how these might be answered. This gives us freedom of choice. The values that we hold provide the means of selecting which pathway we will follow.

Now, the pathways that the human mind can follow vary considerably from the digital computer which we've mentioned before as the problem-solving mechanism of the statistician. These apparatuses have been given their sense of value. They have been told how to use their judgment. And, they do it in a very arbitrary way. We call these instructions "programing." The machines are taught to say "yes" and "no" to a series of questions. Is the object black? Yes or no. Is the person a male? Yes or no. There is no alternative or middle course.

However, it is not this way with the human brain. In the human brain, we are able to answer questions, "Yes" or "No" or "Maybe." This means that there is a "gray zone" between the answer of black or white. When the person has an open mind, he entertains such gray areas of decision. When, however, through prejudice, hate, early circumstances, and fixed beliefs, his mind is closed to all except yes or no, black or white, when there is no gray area of decision possible, then he becomes an intolerant individual. This means that he is very much like a machine—a digital computer that has been taught how to answer questions with no exercise of judgment.

The values that we hold give us a scale by which we can make decisions. It is as though we were asked, "What is the length of this piece of cloth?" If we have a yardstick, we measure it. "What is the weight of this load of sand?" If we have scales, we weigh it. A scale of values gives us the ability to make wise decisions, considered decisions.

In the brief time that we have, I would like to touch on four questions: How are values used in solving problems? How do value judgments bring self-confidence? How do we build strong value systems?

And, how can we keep the value system in good working order?

Dr. Hadley Cantril, a psychologist in Philadelphia, has delved deeply into the subject of the use of value systems in problem-solving. According to him, an outstanding characteristic of man is his capacity to sense values in the quality of his experience. This he calls a "value attribute." This term and the term "assumptive form world," as elaborated in Cantril's book *The Why of Man's Experience,* seem to me such fitting ones that I shall use them freely in this talk.

Most of us have sensed the satisfying values of experience from a job well done; from participating in family, or community, or work projects; from living up to the expectation of our ideals; from struggling toward goals that are higher and that bring us closer to our aspirations. It is particularly true that we sense value attributes in creativity, no matter how it is expressed—a tasty loaf of bread, a room redone in a new way, or perhaps self-expression in one of the arts such as painting, poetry, literature, dramatics.

The ultimate goal of man would seem to be the enhancement of the value attributes of experience. This can be regarded as a sort of top standard of human experience, a standard in its own right. We can think of the process of development in the individual, therefore, as a constant pyramiding of a set of value standards, each one serving as a stepping-stone toward the next experience to come.

Participation in the daily processes of living alters to some extent one's standard of values. For better or for worse, we are building our standard of values according to the way in which we live. Man cannot stand still for long. He must either go forward or slip backward. The standards by which he lives will carry him either toward his aspirations or toward his degradation. If he builds his value system wisely, he will attain individual freedom in the process.

Cantril quotes Carl Rogers as follows:

> "I have yet to find the individual who, when he examines his situation deeply, and feels that he perceives it clearly, deliberately chooses dependence, deliberately chooses to have the integrated direction of himself undertaken by another. When all the elements are clearly perceived, the balance seems invariably in the direction of the painful, but ultimately rewarding, path of self-actualization or growth." [9]

Let us now consider how value judgments build self-confidence. I have often talked to people who confessed that they have no confidence in themselves. Self-assurance, or self-confidence, comes from actually trying things out and finding out whether or not they will work. Values which are accepted and stored, but not tried out, are simply declarations of intention. Our sense of surety is achieved only after we ourselves have successfully overcome past difficulties and know that we know how to meet future ones. As I see it, the real difference between knowledge and wisdom is exactly this. Knowledge which has not been used is still untried. It has not been assessed. But, when knowledge has been used and found to be acceptable, then it becomes wisdom. Wisdom involves value judgments.

This is the primary reason, of course, why purpose in life is so important. As the individual develops aspirations and goals in life, it becomes his highest purpose to experience emergent value attributes.

The net result of our purposeful actions is that we create a whole set of assumptions—our "assumptive form world." These assumptions are our standards, which serve us as guides to future action. For each of us, the only world that we know is created in terms of our assumptions. It is the world that provides what constancy there is in our environment. It is our way of living, our experience of the *consistency* of things, our philosophy of life. This assumptive form world is composed of many different assumptions, built up and integrated into a unified whole. When we talk about integration of self, this is essentially what we mean. Integration of self in terms of a shifting assumptive form world becomes one that involves a dynamic balance as it moves through time.

What we are in our own eyes is largely determined by *our* assumptive form world. What we are in the eyes of other people is largely determined by *their* assumptive form worlds. What every person calls himself is, from a psychological viewpoint, largely made up of his awareness, his loyalties, his expectations, built up by him through his own life and time, and in the particular circumstances in which he has lived.

From this discussion emerges another reason why communication is so important to the problem-solving mechanism of the brain. We cannot be jolted out of our complacency, out of our assumptive form world, unless we experience inconsistencies in the world about us. Inevitably, sooner or later, inconsistencies that become apparent to us, which challenge our assumptive form world, will bring about a change within us. It might be a little change. It might take quite a while in coming. But it will come, because the mind cannot ignore inconsistencies when these are clearly perceived.

How can we build a strong value system? Largely, it must come about during childhood. Parents need to be examples to their children. Children need to participate in the affairs of the family. And always, in family living, change that has a purpose behind it, that makes for things which are better, should be encouraged rather than suppressed. Modification of our assumptive form world, as the scope of our experience is extended, is one of the means by which high-level wellness is maintained.

How can we keep our value system in good working order? This is not easy, because propaganda from a great variety of social forces about us is attempting to penetrate our assumptive form world. These forces are attempting to link their aims, their goals to ours, so that we will interpret them as part and parcel of the values that we have built into our own assumptive form world. This trend of our times tends to create what might be termed a verbal unreality. Words no longer have the meaning once given to them.

I can remember that only a few years ago eggs were classified as pullet, small, medium, and large. The terms "pullet" and "small" have gone completely out of use. Eggs start now at medium and become large, extra large, and, perhaps, jumbo size. Motion pictures are no longer described as important or significant; they are all colossal or supercolossal.

The use of communication for deception and control is not a new thing. It has been employed throughout man's history. However, commercialization of communication by business and by politics would appear to be a fairly recent development. Some advertising techniques not only employ deception about products—a device that merchants have long used—but also have introduced a radically new idea. They try to delude the individual about what his own personal attitudes actually are toward other people and other products. The approach, in effect, tends to undermine the person's ethical and moral sense, and to destroy his assumptive form world as a useful tool.

Time does not permit detailed discussion of the many types of values which are cherished by the individual. We will note only that these tend to fall into four major classes: Survival values, aspirations, values involving associations with others, and ultimate values.

To safeguard the value system which is his, the individual must use it in the day-to-day problems which face him, in the environment where he finds himself. The way he uses his value system to make his judgments will determine whether he functions well or poorly. The selection he makes must be in accord with his purpose in life. Integrity and confidence in self rest upon the individual's scale of values and the judgment that he uses in applying them.

16. IMAGINATION

Today's talk will deal with imagination as a component of the problem-solving mechanism of the mind. Some of you will probably wonder why it is included at all. What has imagination to do with, for instance, the need for communication or the need for data? How does it relate to such things as values, which we discussed in our last talk?

It is my view that imagination is probably the most important of all of these components, because it represents the real breakthrough that man has made over the rest of the animal kingdom, in ability to use his mind to solve problems. How is this true? Because imagination is used in our everyday activities to develop postulates as to possible solutions of problems. This gives us freedom of choice and action. Furthermore, imagination is becoming increasingly creative in its use, and, in this form, it can hold for mankind a future of untold promise.

In the talk today, we will consider four aspects of imagination: its biological base; the role which it plays in problem-solving; the fact that it has been freed in the area of the natural sciences; and the possibilities of greater release of the creative spirit of mankind, so as to penetrate all facets of life and living.

The biological basis for imagination is fantasy. How does imagination differ from fantasy? For purposes of this talk, the term *imagination* will be used in its sense of "mental synthesis of new ideas from elements experienced separately"; while the term *fantasy* will mean illusionary images which are relatively unorganized or unstructured in character.

We are aware that a number of animals experience fantasy. We can see the family pet—the cat or the dog—having dreams as they sleep by the hearthside. However, it is doubtful whether animals have learned to use fantasy in a structured way. It seems to me that fantasy emerges through the interplay of electrical currents between the cortical cells of the brain. Now, obviously many animals, particularly the higher mammals, have a considerable amount of cortex, but very few of them begin to approach in vastness the ten billion cells of the human cortex.

Recent experimentations do indicate that the cortex of the porpoise is approximately of the same order as that of man. Like man, the porpoises are playful animals. We love to see them frolicking around a boat, chasing each other, jumping high into the air.

All humans enjoy several years in their early life which are devoted largely to play and fun. Fantasy and dreams are a part of those early years. Fantasy is real to the young child—at times, more real to him than anything else. To play is the business of a child. The long period of infancy is the ideal situation for fantasy to grow into structured imagination.

Man does not simply live his life from day to day in a matter-of-fact way. He dramatizes it. He enacts it. He lives it over and over again. He creates a plot. He fashions a stage. He peoples the stage with various characters of his imaginings. And, in his imaginings, he tries out first this plot and then that one, until he finds a sequence that suits him. Thus imagination is gradually structured into a useful tool for problem-solving.

A bad habit of our ancestors was to fill up the blank spaces in their experience with demons and all sorts of ugly, fearsome creatures. Myths, reality, and fantasy became confused. Fearful imaginings gave rise to social taboos, and these, in turn, made it difficult for the mind to solve its problems.

Just how does imagination play its role in problem-solving? In everyday living, imagination is more or less a reliable work horse. It occupies itself largely with making postulates. As a specific problem arises that needs solution quickly, the imagination flashes on the screen of consciousness analogous situations previously encountered in life. Possible solutions are made available. Freedom of choice is offered and exercised in terms of action. All of this is done in the fraction of a second.

Now, while imagination is tied down most of the time by this problem-solving necessity, it likes very much to get off and play. It likes to wander in open spaces and enjoy the beauties of nature. The spirit of adventure beckons it on. The inquisitive, probing human mind, building upon its biological and cultural base, urges the individual onward into the unknown. The paradox faced by man in his progress toward new discoveries is the fact that his search is so frequently blocked by deeply held beliefs. Man the discoverer becomes thwarted by man the believer. All too frequently, this means that progress is bogged down in efforts to defend the status quo. Positive values which come from adventuring are replaced by the negative values of just "holding the line."

Modern science has stepped into this gap—this paradox between man the discoverer and man the believer. Science has freed the creative imagination to wander where it will. So long as the scientist deals with just the natural events of life, he can wander without fetters of rigid belief. His creative imagination can soar wherever it wishes. As a result, man's creative imagination has transformed the physical world through the advances of science.

The whole scientific growth in terms of inventions and technology is now on the march at an exponential rate of growth—like compound interest, for instance. On the other hand, we have not freed the creative imagination in connection with social matters and philosophic and religious considerations. Here, we are proceeding at a much slower rate of progress—an arithmetic type of growth.

It seems to me that the problems of mankind, generally speaking, arise from this situation. We cannot go on with uncontrolled exponential growth in connection with science and inventions in the physical world, and remain at such a slow rate of change in our social world.

This brings us to our fourth point, which is: How can the creative spirit of mankind be freed to penetrate all facets of life and living?

What is the creative spirit anyway? This is a tough question. I've defined it in various ways, none of them completely satisfactory. My favorite definition is that the creative spirit is "an expression of self adventuring into the unknown in search of truth." Whatever the definition used, creativeness is man's greatest asset. It behooves man to value highly his creative spirit, to nurture it, and to bring it to maturity, because man's position of dominance stems directly from this quality above all others.

Usually childhood is the time of life in which creativeness buds naturally and can be made to bloom most quickly. Once unleashed within the child, it can become a powerful mechanism to develop the child into a productive and responsible citizen.

Since freeing the creative imagination is so important for the individual and for the development of our science, why do we not make it more important within our social structure? Why do we not honor creative expression? Why not give Oscars for creative minds? Why not give fellowships for especially talented children who are demonstrating creative activity? Why not place creative expression on a pedestal? Why not make it at least equivalent to money, prestige, status, and power? After all, creative expression satisfies something very deep in our nature, and, in the end, it brings to us as individuals a sense of self-fulfillment.

Conformity dominates many phases of our social structure. Some of us, in an effort to keep the status quo, follow it slavishly. Others react violently against it. What we really need within our homes, our families, our communities, and our social institutions is an atmosphere compatible with a certain degree of conformity, but also encouraging creativity. A measure of conformity is necessary to bring stability into living. Creative expression, on the other hand, is absolutely essential if we are to find self-fulfillment. The two are not incompatible. Creativeness can take joy in responsiveness to the social mechanism. Creative expression can bring self-satisfaction to the uniqueness of our personality, and, simultaneously, it can serve our fellow man. It can enhance the cultural heritage for all men.

How can we motivate our people toward creativity? A number of investigators are working to find an answer to this question: A. H. Maslow at Brandeis University, in his researches on self-actualiaztion; Carl Rogers at the Universities of Chicago and Wisconsin, in his efforts to establish a philosophy of counseling consistent with personal growth; Gordon Allport at Harvard University, in his work on the personality theory of "becoming"; Erich Fromm at the University of Mexico, who is deeply concerned with ethics and values in a sane society; Carl Moustakas at the Merrill-Palmer School, who is exploring the possibilities of child-centered play therapy; and a score of others.

All of these workers, each in his own way, lay emphasis on the quality in man's nature which urges him onward toward the actualization of himself— toward the achievement of his full potentialities. This is the surge of life within us, which urges us to grow, to mature, and to pass on to those of our kind what we have learned, so that they in turn can go still further when their lives replace ours. The psychiatrist has shown us that this human tendency to self-actualization may have become deeply buried under layer after layer of encrusted, psychological defense, but that it continues to exist in the tissues of our bodies, awaiting only the proper conditions for release and expression.

The creative imagination of man is the means by which he can explore his future. The mind is his mechanism of evolutionary supremacy. And in the working of the mind, it is the creative imagination which gives man the freedom to choose the path which he will follow.

The creative imagination is man's greatest asset. It must be freed generally and encouraged to go where it will, if we are to move into the potentialities of which we are capable.

Finally, let us remember that *human potential* **is the capacity latent within the individual and society which, when properly triggered or activated along constructive lines, can be released as creative energy for the good of all.**

17. THE SELF

This talk will deal with the self. The concept of self is an important component in problem-solving. If the mind is to arrive at decisions, it needs a focal point around which to operate, and the focal point in this case is the self. It is true that values enter into the decision, and that imagination provides us with a variety of pathways from which we may choose. It is the self, however, which gives us the seat of choice, the reason for choosing.

Now, as I've said before, all of us live in an inner and an outer world. The inner world is the world of insight; and the outer world, the world of perception.

Perception by the individual depends upon a recognition of both his inner and his outer world. I think of the self as being perched between these two worlds, overlooking both the inside and the outside. The overview by self of both its worlds must be experienced in panoramic fullness and perceived in depth.

The self that reviews both its inner and its outer world must be a balanced and a fearless self.

All of us tend to *think* that we are very objective in the way we look at the outside world. We see it, we hear it, and that is what it is. However, all of these sensations that we receive from the outside world are interpreted according to what we have in the inner world. And when it comes to the inner world, few of us see in depth. Actually, to explore one's self inside is one of the most fascinating and rewarding of experiences, particularly if the exploration is undertaken in a spirit of adventure and without fear.

Why should we fear our inner world? It is there. It is going to influence our decisions and our perceptions, so we ought to become well acquainted with it.

The perception laboratories of the psychologists have proved beyond any shadow of doubt that perception is a two-way process. What we see or feel in the outside world is conditioned by concepts and attitudes based on experiences of a similar nature that have been recorded in our inner world. And, when we meet up with happenings in the outer world which contradict what we believe, this invariably brings about a certain amount of change in our inner world.

Let's have a closer look at how this self, perched between the inside world and the outside world, operates. I'll have to confess to you a silly little game that I frequently play. I think of this self as a person. He's equipped with radar and can scan outwards or inwards. He's always busy. Even when I'm asleep, he's at work. And, he's very serious. I call him Mr. S. R., for "self-radar," and I treat him with a great deal of courtesy. We respect each other. At times, when I'm troubled about some problem, I'll say to him, "Mr. S. R., what should I do in this kind of situation? I just don't see the answer." He mumbles back, "Well, I'll see what I can do about it." It may be several days later, but he always comes up with some sort of answer, and almost always it's unanticipated—something that my conscious mind didn't get at all. I suppose this is what we call intuitive thought.

An experience bearing on this comes to mind, from several years ago. I was returning to Washington from Detroit by plane, and had settled back in my seat, when a thin, grayish man sat down beside me. He looked tired. There were lines in his face. He sank into sleep almost immediately. Pretty soon, the stewardess woke us up for breakfast, and we started to talk. My traveling companion proved to be a well-known scientist and mathematician. I recalled Poincaré's thesis on mathematical creation, and asked him what his ideas were on the subject of intuitive thought. Many persons doubt whether there is such a thing.

My companion said, "Oh, of course there is. I use it all the time. When I face a tough problem I try to define exactly what the problem is and where I want to go in terms of its solution. Then I load my mind with all the data I can get that are pertinent to this problem. After that, I simply put it out of my conscious mind altogether. And, sooner or later, the answer comes. It may be the next day, or perhaps several days or even a week or two later, but eventually the answer will pop into my mind. As soon as the idea comes, I proceed to do something about it, with all the conscious equipment at my command. I analyze it to see what, if any, loopholes there are, but usually the solution is the 'right' one. I'm a great believer in intuitive thought. I wouldn't try to solve problems without it."

Now, I should like to emphasize here that intuitive thought can't work without all of the rest of the components of problem-solving. You must have access to the data that you need. You must try to examine as much data as possible bearing on the problem. Your channels of communication must be kept open. You must be able to talk with people who are sharing similar ideas. Your senses must be sharpened to perceive everything that is pertinent to the particular problem which you wish to solve. The values that you hold and the imagination which you use to formulate possible hypotheses for the solution of the problem are very essential. When you finally turn to your "self-radar" for help, all of these things should be available to it to "play around with."

There's a very important point that I'd like to bring to your attention at this stage. The self is not the same as the self-concept. Dr. S. I. Hayakawa makes this point very nicely. As he puts it:

> "The fundamental motive of human behavior is not self-preservation but the preservation of the symbolic self. . . . The basic purpose of all human activity is the protection, the maintenance, and the enhancement, not of the self but of the self-concept or the symbolic self."[10]

This author then goes on to cite a passage from Oliver Wendell Holmes' *Autocrat at the Breakfast Table,* in which Holmes observed that in any encounter between two individuals there are actually six persons present. First, there are John and William. Then there are John's idea of John and William's idea of William, which may be entirely different from John and William. And then, third, there are John's idea of William, and William's idea of John, which amounts to six "persons" altogether. This is a perceptive idea. Notice that John, therefore, acts not in his own interest, but his interests as he sees them in terms of his self-concept, which may not be the same thing as his own interest. And William, too, acts in the interest of his self-concept, but possibly not of his actual self.

Throughout our infancy, childhood, and youth, we struggle in more or less ceaseless effort to adjust ourselves to a world of adults. We are always struggling with fear—fear of being alone, fear of falling, fear of dark places, fear of animals, fear of people, a thousand kinds of fears. Usually, as the child grows up, these fears recede into the background of memory until they're forgotten by the conscious mind—forgotten though they lurk beneath the surface of thought and attack when least expected.

I remember various such fears from my childhood, as I'm sure you must too. I was terrified of spiders. It all started one day at the corner grocery store. The grocer had bottled up a huge, hairy tarantula, which, sluggish from cold, had lurked in a bunch of bananas. Day after day, I would go to the store and gaze at this hairy monster, until it left me with an almost hynotic fear, something which was there all the time, which I could see in my dreams.

Now, in the concept of myself that I built up, there was a statement, "I am not afraid of spiders." I'd go out of my way to crush spiders. This typifies what we try to do when we build up a concept of our self. We tend to put into this stereotype the opposite of our real fears. Almost 50 years passed before I learned that this fear was buried in my tissues, and took steps to bring it to the surface and deal with it.

Perhaps this well illustrates why Sidney Jourard's work on self-disclosure, at the University of Florida, is so important. He is conducting studies on how much and what we disclose of our inner selves to other persons—to our parents, to our mate, to our close friends. His findings suggest that, to the extent that we are able to disclose ourselves to others, we get relief from inner tension.

Hayakawa states the problem this way: One of the things a person tends to do is to rigidify his self-concept and to protect it, rather than assessing his true self. Example: "I am the best salesman in this company, no matter what the records show."

Now, let's say that this concept of self has become fairly well rigidified so that the self-concept stays put for a while. The trouble is that the self won't stay put. It keeps slipping away from the self-concept, and consequently, as time goes on, the person's ideas about himself become less and less real. In other words, at the beginning it may have been true that the individual under discussion was the best salesman in the company. But time changes everything, and, with the passing of the years, he is no longer the best salesman in the company, even though he conceptualizes himself as such.

This type of delusion is particularly true in the older ages. So many, many people keep living in the glories of their past. And yet, self-fulfillment and self-satisfaction at these ages come from what one is, and not from what one was.

Perhaps you will recall that in an earlier talk we discussed the awareness axis. This was defined as the dynamic balance of an integrated self, maintained as a moving axis of equilibrium between the various energy fields which affect the individual, both from within and without. We can now see more clearly why "Mr. S. R.", situated at the junction of the inner and the outer worlds, is in a fine position to do his scanning. When thus balanced, he can cast his radar beams both outside and inside the body.

At times, the pressures of life become so severe that a person will retreat entirely within himself. In such a case "Mr. S. R." can cast his beam only on the inside world, which means that all of its fears, its dreams, its imaginings, its distortions will be the subject of his reports.

As the concept of your self becomes removed from actuality, you enter unreality. The picture of yourself no longer has any relationship to the actuality that is you. The road to mental health requires that you be able to face the facts about yourself. To see yourself as others see you is of particular help, here.

High-level wellness for the individual involves integrity of self. You cannot have integrity of self if your self-concept is of such an order that it is not consistent with what you are. Love thy neighbor as thy self—this command has come down to us throughout the centuries. But, you cannot love thy self unless you have respect for your own integrity, your own uniqueness, your own concepts, and what you are. You cannot be on good terms with your fellow man, with your wife, with your children, unless you are on good terms with yourself. This is an absolute necessity, in the human relationships between people.

To conclude this talk, I would like to come back to problem-solving. We want our minds to be good problem-solvers in the light of actuality. We want to be able to depend upon them to select the "right" solution for the particular problem, from a larger number of possible solutions. To enable "Mr. S. R." to do the very best job possible, taking into account both inside and outside factors, our self-concept must be rooted in reality.

18. BALANCE AND INTEGRATION OF SELF

This talk deals with balance and the integration of self. It thus involves both the mind as a problem-solving mechanism and the body as a manifestation of organized energy.

I have already pointed out that high-level wellness involves the total individual—the body, the mind, and the spirit as a totality. Also, that the integration of the self, which is so essential to the state of high-level wellness, can best be achieved when the body is in balance—when the energy forces of the body are free to flow where they will, to reach equilibrium.

In much the same way, problems are best solved when the mind is in balance and at rest, rather than when it is in focus. I know this is quite the opposite from our stereotype of what the thinker is. We are inclined, when we talk about thinking, to think of concentration. We see the figure of Rodin's "The Thinker," for instance, as a person pondering intensely, shutting everything out of his mind except the matter in hand. Now this kind of thinking is a part of the process; but it is only a part.

As I see it, there are five main steps in the solution of a problem. The *first* of these is to define the problem, understand what it is, and set up some goal towards which one is reaching. The *second* step is to obtain the data necessary for the solution of the problem. This may come from library research, from conferences, from consultation with people who are likely to know something about it. The *third* step, then, might be that of the thinker. You concentrate at this stage. You try to put up various structures which might satisfy the requirements.

As I see it, the *fourth* step involves the inner workings of the mind. The mind has a probability mechanism more or less like the giant computers which we have mentioned before. Perhaps there are millions upon millions of possible solutions which must be touched upon. This part of the process is done at terrific speed by the mind, and quite unconsciously. Ultimately, an answer will come. We call this process intuition. For purposes of intuitive thought, the mind needs a body which is balanced and relaxed, in order to free the imagination to probe deeply in all directions.

Remember, the self-radar station that I mentioned in my last talk is casting its beam over the entire mental track. It is working diligently night and day to turn up data which might bear upon the problem. It does this work best at times of relaxation. When the brain is working at a focus, the channels are narrow; but when it is at rest, it can work broadly throughout the whole field of probability integration, in order to get the best possible answer.

It is interesting to speculate on what alerts the brain to a particular solution. Why is it that the brain suddenly picks out a particular solution from the many, many millions of probabilities which it is contacting at breakneck speed, and knows "this is it"?

What is this intuitive process of thought which suddenly produces an idea recognizable as the "right" answer? Poincaré suggests, and I'm inclined to agree with him, that it is the recognition of beauty—that is, beauty in a mathematical sense, a beauty of harmony that comes from everything fitting together as an integrated whole. From the monotonous dullness of thousands and perhaps millions of possible solutions examined and discarded, the beauty of a particular solution which integrates things as a whole stands out in bold relief, and the mind says, "This looks like *it*. Let's examine it in more detail."

At this point, the intuitive mind passes the ball back to the conscious mind. It is now the job of the mind to *test* the intuitive thought. The testing is the *fifth* step in the problem-solving device. After all, while intuitive thought is usually right, sometimes it isn't. Sometimes beauty is there without having a perfect solution. However, it is the job of the conscious mind and of the logical processes to pick this intuitive idea to pieces, to test it in every way possible, and to build it into a solid block of knowledge which will support the solution.

The need of the mind for balance and relaxation as an integral part of its power to solve problems is paralleled by the need of the body for balance and relaxation as an integral part of the way it maintains its energy organization.

Perhaps I should pause here to give a definition of the word "balance" in its broadest sense. *Balance* is the moving axis of equilibrium between the interrelated and interacting energy fields of body, mind, spirit, and environment. As mentioned before, everything inside of the body and outside of the body is constantly shifting and changing. It would be utterly impossible to maintain balance unless the balance was dynamic. Dynamic balance or equilibrium involves a continuity of change. Dynamic equilibrium cannot be maintained in a state of fixation. It involves action and direction. It's like a spinning top. It has a very good balance while it is spinning; but, when the spin ceases, it wobbles and falls to the floor.

In the human being and his mental processes, we are involved with action, direction, and purpose. Consequently, the equilibrium that we maintain in our lives and in our thought processes can only be reintegrated as the dynamic balance of a changing self.

The physical energy available to the body is also maintained in balance. In another talk, we observed that the magic of life is involved with the ability of the living organism to extract energy from the physical environment and to use it for the purposes of life. Balance is needed in this operation. During the waking hours, the individual tends to use up expendable energy at a faster rate than it can be extracted from food and other sources, and, consequently, he must call on some of the reserves of glycogen or of fat to fill in the deficit.

One of the functions, then, of rest and sleep is to allow time for the storage rate of expendable energy to catch up and to recharge the individual's "batteries" with a full potential of expendable energy which he can use in the active hours of the coming day. The operation is something like that of a flashlight. You wouldn't think of leaving the light on all the time, because if you did the battery would run down.

So long as you are alive, the body and the mind are in action. Whether you're waking or sleeping, the blood is circulating, the food is digesting, the nerve impulses are traveling, the muscles are tensing and releasing, the glands are functioning, and the body cells are performing their metabolic functions. Everything is activity.

At night, when you sleep, things slow down a bit. It is easier for the different parts of the body to communicate with each other when there is balance between the tensions of living and the gentler activities of relaxation—such as play and entertainment, vacation, humor, laughter, and the quiet enjoyment of aesthetic interests. Under such conditions, we are able to change ourselves more easily, and a more favorable environment for the reintegration of self is afforded.

The moving axis of dynamic equilibrium, with its absence of strife and haste, fosters sensitive awareness, understanding, insight, aesthetic appreciation, altruism, and love. Rarely can a depth of understanding between two people be arrived at in the rush of a busy day. I'm sure you would all agree with me that it's far better to court one's sweetheart under the light of the moon than with a telephone clutched in both hands. The strongest human ties spring from this state of balance. When time is taken for appreciation of mutual interests, friendship ripens into companionship and love.

Balance, after all, is the womb of freedom. It starts, of course, with a pretty thorough knowledge of one's self—something difficult to achieve. But, without a knowledge of one's inner self, understanding of the outer world cannot have breadth and depth.

A mind that is tortured with prejudice and hate and fear projects itself in disturbed human relationships. Although the psychiatrists have done much to relieve the twisted minds of the mentally ill, little has been undertaken to help ordinary people, classified as well, to know themselves and thus become better balanced and better able to meet their daily problems. How much of the demand for sleeping pills, alcohol, and tranquilizers is due to this deep-felt need? This is a real problem, and one that we must come to grips with.

To conclude then, a state of balance within the body and the mind serves three vital purposes. First, it is the medium in which intuitive thought processes operate, to serve us in the solution of problems. Second, it is the state in which the energy fields of the body arrive at dynamic equilibrium. And third, it is the condition in which physical energy forces and the currents of the mind are harmonized and built into an integrated whole.

In these terms *mental health* **becomes synonymous with physical health, spiritual health, and social health, and can be defined as balance maintained between the interacting and interrelated energy fields of body-mind-spirit and the environment.**

We must make room for balance in our lives. We need sleep and rest in proper quantities. We need relaxation between periods of tension. We need to intersperse work and leisure. A balanced life is a good life. And, furthermore, it is an effective life. It is more effective in terms of the way we use our body. We do not age so rapidly. Our older years are more effective. And, we do a better job of solving our problems, throughout life.

Here, then, is further proof to support our definition that high-level wellness means functioning at a level of high potential. The problem is, how can we **bring a greater achievement of such functioning into** our daily lives? Certainly balance and self-integration are essential ingredients, and both pay off in a very handsome way.

19. MATURITY IN WHOLENESS

Today's talk on "Maturity in Wholeness" is another in the series devoted to the mind as a problem-solving mechanism. In it, I shall take up four questions: What is meant by maturity in wholeness? Why is maturity in wholeness a component of the problem-solving mechanism? How does maturity in wholeness develop? And, what are the principal manifestations of maturity in wholeness?

In considering what is meant by maturity in wholeness, let us go back to the definition of totality given in our talk on "The Nature of Man." We said that the individual is a total personality, consisting of a continuum of body, mind, and spirit within an ever-changing environment and flow of events. Later, in the talk on "The Emergent Mind," we defined the mind as the ability-complex of man to use his inner world for the purpose of solving the problems of everyday living.

Earlier talks have given considerable attention to the meaning of body and mind, but we have hardly more than touched on the meaning of "spirit" as that term is used in these talks. By "spirit" I do not mean to imply a metaphysical or religious entity, but rather the vitality of the person—his will to do things, his aliveness, as it were.

Now, most of us have experienced from time to time a period of supreme aliveness. I know that at such times, when everything is right within me, when my body is well and my thoughts are in tune with the world, my spirit soars with the joy of living. Every sense organ in me is wide open to drink in the impressions of all that I see and feel and hear. And at such times, I actually feel intoxicated with the ecstasy of just being alive. No task is too difficult; no hurdle, too high.

There are many examples of what high spirit means to the individual. Let me give you just one. As a doctor, I've been impressed many times by how important the attitude of the patient is to his recovery. Most doctors know, for instance, how important it is for the patient to have confidence in his physician. Usually, when the doctor feels that the patient has lost faith in him, he does something about it. He may transfer the patient to another physician, or at least call in some other physician for consultation.

In discussing the role of the spirit in connection

with human wellness, Dr. Sidney Jourard, a psychologist in the University of Florida, has drawn attention to the fact that there are several elements invariably present when the person is functioning at a high level. One of these is respect by others of his individuality. Another is that he is the recipient of love. All of us need love in our life, and when we receive it, from whatever source, it seems to "do something" that lifts our spirits to a higher level. Assuming rudimentary health habits, Jourard goes on to say that it is doubtless true that high-spirited persons become ill less often than low-spirited ones; and that persons with much to live for—who love deeply and broadly, and who draw on their inner resources to solve the mysteries of the universe and to satisfy the needs and wants of mankind—probably live longer than less dedicated people.

Now, maturity in wholeness is maturity in the wholeness of body, mind, and spirit, taken all together. The degree of wisdom that one attains in life depends very largely upon the degree of maturity in wholeness that he achieves. The interrelatedness of the human organism, which is wholeness, must grow just like the body grows. And, maturity of adulthood in the older years is related to wholeness, and must also grow.

As I view it, maturity is not a fixed ceiling upon our potential; it is an ever-expanding one. Maturity in wholeness is never absolute; it is always relative.

A person who is a teenager can have maturity in wholeness at his particular age level, and be doing his very best. And, a person at age 90 can still have a meaningful future before him. He can still not have achieved the sum total of maturity in wholeness of which he is capable.

A truly mature person can actually live up to the golden rule of human relationship: "Whatsoever ye would that men should do unto you, do ye even so unto them." Perhaps there is also a golden rule of the mind, which might be phrased something like this: Endeavor each day to know yourself better, to keep an open mind, and to continually reexamine beliefs or practices in the light of contradictions which come to your attention. As indicated in previous talks, living up to this would make it possible for us to readjust our beliefs or practices into an integrated and consistent whole. It would enable us to arrive at a new level of adjustment or harmony. This is what maturity means.

Why is maturity in wholeness a component of the problem-solving mechanism? The answer is simple. Think back to the analogy of the watch. We examined various elements of the structure of the watch. The watch, regardless of the perfection of its separate parts, must work together as a whole. Likewise, maturity in wholeness, since it involves the interrelatedness of all of the parts of the mind, becomes itself a component of the problem-solving mechanism.

Let us now address ourselves to the third question: How does maturity in wholeness develop? Well, I think it has to grow. Infants must have the loving care of a mother in the early months after birth. It has been well demonstrated, for instance, that there is an enormous difference between home care and institutional care for foundlings. Babies need to be fussed over and given loving care. Without mother love, they tend to draw into themselves, and a far higher proportion of them die.

It has been demonstrated by research work along these lines that when a nurse can take the time to be a sort of alter-mother—to play with the baby, fondle it, love it up a bit—the baby will respond, and such handling can make a difference in the mortality rate as between home care and institutional care.

In order to develop healthy personalities, certain needs basic to our nature must be satisfied. We must have open sense organs so that we can get information into ourselves from the outside world. We must have interchange with other people, because, after all, they are human beings and we learn what a human being is like by being with human beings. I am told that the little goslings, when they are hatched and reared completely by a human, start following around the person who cares for them just as though he was their mother. They seem to think of themselves as human beings. When we are young, most of us tend to think of ourselves as like the person most closely associated with our rearing.

From infancy on, each person grows outward in ever-widening circles of experience. He continues to add new experiences to his accumulated fund of knowledge. Consequently, he does not stop at any point. There is always some part of each person which still feels the needs of the infant, the needs of the child, the frustrations of the teenager, the difficulties and unsolved problems of the adolescent. Each part of the ever-extending and growing personality needs its particular types of satisfactions and has its particular types of difficulties.

These are some of the reasons, then, that maturity in wholeness must grow. Maturity in wholeness for the child is not the same as that of the teenager. And, the degree of maturity in wholeness achieved by the young adult must ripen slowly into the wisdom of the older ages. The spiritual aspects of growing in wholeness are involved largely with determining our responsibility and our place in the scheme of things. This is the way we learn to have faith in ourselves. If you cannot understand yourself, if you are always running away from yourself, you cannot respect yourself. And, unless you respect yourself in this sense, you do not have personal integrity or personal dignity. You tend to accuse other people of all of the things that are really the matter with you.

This is a paradox, but, nevertheless, it is the way our minds work; and we must come to grips with it if we are to achieve maturity in wholeness.

Now, for our last question: What are the principal manifestations of maturity in wholeness? In my view, they are five in number: First, the degree to which a person is able to develop *conceptual thought*. The baby is not born with conceptual thought. It has to grow. And this ability to think of things conceptually starts developing at about the age of three. It goes on growing, during all of a person's life. And, as the individual becomes more and more complex, his ability to think conceptually in abstract ways increases correspondingly.

The second manifestation we shall call *systems formation of knowledge*. For most of us, this usually involves one or two disciplines. We educate ourselves to become scientists, technologists, philosophers, religious leaders, or for a variety of other professions.

Self-integration becomes necessary if we are to have maturity, and the degree that we are able to achieve it and maintain it is a measure of our maturity.

Group integration—the way we are able to interrelate ourselves with group living and with others—is also a very important factor.

And finally comes *purpose*—purpose in life—because with deepening patterns of knowledge, understanding, and wisdom, we find it increasingly necessary to interrelate into broader total patterns our conceptual-thought patterns and the systems formation of knowledge which we have. It is only by solving our problems in a *total* way that we can come to solutions for many of the complexities of living.

Maturity in wholeness, then, involves a knowledge of one's self, understanding of others, and a harmony resulting from these two realities.

20. PURPOSE

This talk on "Purpose" is the last of the ten dealing with the mind as a problem-solving mechanism. In it, I shall take up three questions: Why is purpose important in problem-solving? What conditions bring purpose into living? And, how is purpose transforming mankind?

To the first question—"Why is purpose important in problem-solving?"—I believe that there are at least two answers. The first answer is that purpose tends to spur the problem-solving mechanism into excellence of performance. When we struggle for a goal, when our life has purpose, we mature more quickly and more completely. We do the very best of which we are capable. This striving brings performance to a high level. The second answer is that striving also develops the mind to use its latent capacity for intuitive thought—that is, it stimulates full use of the creative imagination.

Thus, purpose aids the mind to evolve into a more efficient problem-solving mechanism—to attain an ever-higher level of competence in which it is able to view problems as total entities. In part, this is due to the fact that purpose brings with it courage— courage to adventure ever further, to cross the boundaries of systematic knowledge, and to move toward the outer reaches of creative or cosmic consciousness.

Now for the question: "What conditions bring purpose into living?" In part, these conditions arise in the outer world and are related to a great variety of natural and cosmological energy fields, which act through their directional lines of force. In part, they are also related to numerous social energy fields in the outer world, through the lines of influence beamed on us from the various organizations of which we are a part.

The effects of the energy fields through which we pass, both natural and cosmic, have already been explored in the talk on man as a manifestation of organized energy. Lines of force bring direction, a form of purpose, to the responding energy fields of the tissues of our bodies. In general, we recoil from destructive energies, but respond to those which please us. We resist the pressures of constricted space, but respond to the freedom of open spaces. These, and thousands of similar reactions, are the tangible effects of interaction between the energy fields of our bodies and those of the outer world through which we move.

Social lines of influence are also force fields in their way. The mind of man tends to follow the polarized lines of influence of the social organizations in which he is a participant. Likewise, smaller groups of men tend to follow the lines of influence of larger organizations of which they are a part.

Space is important in both the natural and the social energy fields. Contraction of space within these fields occurs when the force poles move closer together. The effect is to give greater direction to the lives of those falling under such influences. It would appear that one of our great needs is to get space back into daily living. Social man is violating, on every side, the space needs of the individual. Even the wild animals recognize their need for living space and fight for it. When people are jammed too closely together, tensions rise and they become quarrelsome. The boundary lines of two hostile nations should be insulated until their leaders can sit around the council table and talk things over in an atmosphere relatively free of tension.

The powerful force of love is another condition which brings purpose into living. Perhaps this is just another kind of energy, but in any event it affects both the outer and the inner worlds of man. Love starts in the family. And, as we love, we learn to have trust and faith in those whom we love. Faith in our fellow man leads to the fellowship of man, and this in turn leads to the great concept of oneness of life.

Purpose comes into life from the inner world of man through his creative use of the imagination. It is, in effect, directional creativity applied within a force field. The creative imagination tends to be restricted by the social lines of influence. Given relative freedom, however, and strong interests of his own, the individual will develop the creative quality of his imagination. As such development becomes an increasingly important factor in his life, inner purpose is generated and streams outward. Furthermore, it brings the satisfaction of self-fulfillment, since it is an expression of the uniqueness which is a component of man's nature.

A fundamental gap in the world today is the lack of purposes and goals which can appeal to mankind everywhere, irrespective of nation, race, or creed. If our split-up, strife-torn world is ever going to work as a whole, in even a semblance of harmony, something must emerge which will constitute an energy field or an influence field surrounding mankind *as a whole*.

It seems to me that the trouble with our present fragmented world is that while we need world union—at least to the degree of maintaining a world commonwealth of cooperating nations—we are not willing to pay the price for it. Ultimately, survival needs might be strong enough to bring this about.

But I doubt this, **because survival** is primarily oriented in a negative direction—a Maginot line of defensive fortresses. What is needed is an all-important, *positive purpose* for mankind—one which will challenge men everywhere and appeal to the best in them; one which will produce a striving for a common goal; one which will permit ties of comradeship to grow in a friendly world.

"Coexistence" needs to be replaced by the concept of "cooperative adventuring."

The conditions which bring purpose into living, then, involve a blending of forces such as: the energy fields of society, nature, and the as-yet-vaguely-defined cosmic elements in the outer world; the great radial force of love, as it streams outward toward our fellow man; and the releasing of the creative imagination within the individual, which also reaches outward, ever farther, toward the mysteries of the universe.

Now for the final question: "How is purpose transforming man?" In an earlier talk, we dealt with the natural evolution of the human being and pointed out that, because of man's culture, natural evolution has slowed down with respect to bodily phenomena. Races which originally started to be divergent are now moving closer together. This is because the social order has shrunk the world. Communication among the various parts of the world is bringing about a mingling of the races of man, and mankind is in the process of becoming literally one race.

We also pointed out that there is one area—the human mind—in which natural evolution is still a very active force. The human mind is still emerging. In the course of time, we can look forward to a type of man who is able to use his mind in a far more effective manner than at present.

The world of man is in urgent need of achieving this higher stage of mental development—a stage which we have termed "creative consciousness." You will recall that in our talk on the emergence of the mind, previous layers of consciousness were described: sensitivity, which we share with all living creatures; simple consciousness, involving percepts, recepts, and the naming of classified groups; and conceptual consciousness, which involves language and abstract symbolization, and which leads to logic. From these tools, we have built our culture and accumulated our systematic bodies of knowledge.

Through developing various analytical tools, we have now begun to sense the interrelatedness of all problems. The human mind as a problem-solving mechanism, therefore, is grappling with how to get interrelatedness into the solution of problems. The solution of many problems simply cannot be arrived at unless the creative imagination is allowed to probe freely in various directions, crossing the boundary lines of systematic collections of knowledge.

With the birth of science, a great change has come about which is releasing the creative spirit of man. Formerly, creativeness had to live within the particular dogmas and faiths of its culture; but science took as its faith the search for truth, and unleashed creativity. The entire strength of science rests upon its dedication to the search for truth, and upon its discipline of approaching such truth through successive approximations to the truth, each approximation a little closer than its predecessor.

Dynamic progress can come only from a never-ending search for truth and a willingness to accept new facts when they have been proven. Accepting new facts means readjustment of theories held in the past. This, in turn, paves the way for integration of the new facts with the old, and for the elevation of theories to a higher level.

What are the purposes which will challenge youth? Which are those needed in early adulthood? What are the purposes which could revitalize the older years of life? Our job now is to search for those purposes, goals, and projects which will nurture the mind of man throughout his life cycle, and which will unite mankind, not in a negative but in a positive way. Purposes which will stimulate the imagination, which will hold forth the thrill of adventure and the promise of helping man to find fulfillment. The Geophysical Year was such a project; but a year was too short. Why not a Geophysical Century? Or per-

158

haps a century of biological research so that men
everywhere can come to understand life more fully?
Man should be a leader of the life process, the responsible custodian of the life force.

Let us pursue those aims which will further the
development of a creative consciousness adequate to
cope with the problems of our times and to chart new
pathways into the future.

21. INDIVIDUAL WELLNESS

Today, I would like to summarize what has gone ahead. Our subject is "Individual Wellness," and, of course, this represents the sum total of what we've considered, up to now.

Perhaps the best way to start is by reviewing the definition of high-level wellness. You will recall that we used the base definition of health given in the preamble of the Constitution of the World Health Organization. As developed in this series of talks, high-level wellness for the individual is conceived as a direction in progress forward and upward, toward a higher potential of functioning; an open-ended and ever-expanding tomorrow which involves a challenge to live at a fuller potential. It also involves the integration of the whole being of the person—his body, his mind, and his spirit—in the functioning process.

Now, we talked first of all about the importance of the nature of man with respect to this concept, and we developed this at some length in connection with particular elements of man's nature. We developed the idea that man is a child of energy, and pointed out the very great importance of energy fields because they interlock and interpenetrate one another. The energy fields of our body are interrelated with those of our family and our community, and, in fact, with everything that goes on around us in the physical world. Because of this, we live in both an inner and an outer world.

It is our particular responsibility to take care of our inner world and to know a great deal about it. Most of us concentrate upon doing things in the outer world, but, actually, our inner world, made up of cells organized into a "cooperative commonwealth," very largely controls how we operate in the outer world. The cells of the body work together. They work together because in that way they get what they need to do their job.

We brought out that these little cellular worlds are very unusual, extraordinary molecular worlds. They are efficient chemical factories which take the energy which we give to them and transform it into the kinds of energy we need for our processes of living. We ought to be proud of them. We ought to take care of them. And, if this thing that we call "I" means anything at all, it means that we must be responsible for doing the things which should be done for these hard-working cells that are our body. If we take care of them properly, they will do the best possible job they can for us.

Then we took up, in succeeding talks, some things about the importance of biology, particularly the life cycle that man goes through. He starts as a fertilized egg cell. He grows into a tremendous aggregate of cells, roughly estimated at 100 trillion cells, all of which have to work together. Over the course of his life, energy and information are taken into his body and used for the purposes of living. He discovers that, as the life cycle progresses, aging effects are more and more in evidence, and that aging really is a phenomenon of energy trying to escape its confines. The body gets brittle, and it becomes increasingly difficult to keep it together as an organized whole. We have learned that heredity plays its part in this picture.

Next, we touched briefly upon the importance of society and of the physical environment about us. These are important because the society in which we live, and the various institutions, such as the family and the community and the job, all have their part to play in connection with keeping the body well. They generate lines of influence which affect us. So, we must be concerned about the social environment.

The physical environment also must concern us, because it has an effect upon our ability to grow and to live useful lives. If the environment is too hostile, we find that we can't survive as organized human energy systems. If it is too favorable, we tend to go soft. So, we would like for our environment to be challenging. It should have problems in it. It should have excitement in it. And, it should always carry a future with something to do.

Now, a good share of our previous talks have been devoted to the matter of the mind—what it is, how it has emerged as a part of this body in which we find ourselves, how it works. We know that use of the imagination is a part of the problem-solving process; that values are also essential, if we are to select the best course of action. We know that the concept of our self, which we build up, has been made possible through the use of the imagination. And, we have come to realize that the mind of man is still evolving—rather rapidly, in fact—so that achievement by the individual of high-level wellness depends, to a considerable degree, on keeping the body and mind in step with each other. The body is evolving also, of course, but at a much slower pace. Consequently, integration of the mind and body must be allowed to shift and adjust and readapt, if the two are to be kept in step.

If we can achieve this self-integration, this balance, then our body is well. On the other hand, if we don't do a good job of being integrated, then we begin to misuse and misdirect the energy which is available to us—it becomes destructive; it goes berserk; it destroys tissues. These effects of misused and mis-directed energy are the cause of psychosomatic illness, which is most of human sickness.

At this point, let us review, briefly, some of the basic needs of man—basic needs, because they are part of man's nature. First of all, we have to survive. Unless we can keep our body together as an organized whole, we die. Therefore, survival is all-important. This means that we must have enough food. We must protect ourselves against harmful energy. And, we must get rid of waste material. For the race, it means that we must pass on our biological heritage to our children, and this needs to be passed on in a form which is not destructive to them.

It is very important that we have adequate communication with the outside world. Our sense organs need to be open. They need to be highly sensitive. We know that sensory ports for information close down in the older years. Our sight grows feeble. Our hearing grows weak. Consequently, communication becomes an increasingly important problem as one gets older.

Fellowship with other human beings is also very important. All of us are lonely in our inner world. We reach out for our fellow man in order to have the companionship which makes life worth living. This is one of the strengths of mankind. His ability to work with other people, to get along with them, is one of the reasons he has been able to attain a very high position in the animal world.

The importance of growth has been stressed. Life is an emerging phenomenon. We grow from a protected position to an ever-broadening horizon. This is the reason the child must find a secure place within the family circle before he can become really accustomed to, and useful in, the broader social pattern of the school and of the community. As people grow old, they need to retreat into a relatively more secure position, something that is safer and not so bustling, because this is a part of the physical slowing-down process. But, it is very important—we've brought this out again and again—that, as the individual advances in years, his mind keeps on growing even when his body continues to weaken. Therefore, it is important to people, as they grow older, to supplant the active physical interests of their younger years and become more deeply interested in the concerns of mankind, in the affairs of their community, and in passing on to others the qualities and incentives that will aid them, in turn, to live their lives to the full.

Time does not permit more than fleeting mention of various other basic needs which we've touched upon in earlier talks. Love is a vital factor in our lives. We cannot achieve high-level wellness without it. Imagination and values are a part of our mental processes. We can't solve our problems without both qualities. And, it is extraordinarily important that our lives have some degree of balance in them. Without balance, it is difficult to have and to exercise freedom. We need to meditate at times. We need to commune with the universal. This is what religion really is. We need to develop a philosophy of life that makes living worthwhile for us.

And so, we come to the conclusion of this summary, with the realization that the basic needs of man are also the ingredients of high-level wellness for the individual. In the satisfaction of these needs, we shall satisfy the dictates of our nature.

22. FAMILY WELLNESS

This time, I would like to give one of several talks in this series, on high-level wellness as it relates to *groups* of persons. It seems to me that family wellness ought to head the list. After all, the family stands in between individual wellness and social wellness. You can't really have high-level wellness for either individuals or social groups unless you have well families.

Why are families important? First of all, because, as a biological unit, the family is responsible for reproduction, and ensures the survival of the human race. We all know that certain service functions, in earlier days performed by families, have now been taken over by agencies outside the family. But, there are other service functions left, which society feels can best be provided by the family. Let's look at them.

It would appear that, in addition to its biological purpose, the modern family serves at least two additional, vital functions in society. It rears the children; and it provides an emotional setting for stabilization of the adolescent and the adult personality. Now, the relation of this to high-level wellness is a very direct one. Since the family provides the setting for these two purposes, optimum performance in the family could avert many of the strains and maladjustments that now require pediatric, general medical, and psychiatric service for both children and adults.

Now, what is family wellness? It has the same elements in it that high-level wellness for the individual has. There must be a direction that the family is taking which is forward and upward. There must be a future for the family, with opportunity for it to develop its full potential. The family must be integrated, so that it can operate with wholeness in meeting its problems. It must not be just a collection of individuals held together by convenience.

Unless children have the protection and the security of a family which loves them, it is very hard for them to grow up to be normal adults. So, the child should be able to equate family with love. To the adult father and mother, the home should be the place they come back to each day, and renew their confidence in themselves and in each other. And finally, the family should be the bulwark of security for all its members. On the whole, we live in a hostile world, and it is the family circle which gives us the sense of security that enables us to face the world intelligently and with confidence.

The family, then, is first of all the cradle of the life cycle itself. It's a small world. It starts with two people, and, as the children come along, it evolves into a little group—a place where "everybody knows everybody." It's a safe world for the child to develop in, and it's a loving world. The child, on his part, must learn to love, for without this his later life can not be full and rich and mature.

When you feel safe and secure, then the environment out beyond you is attractive to you. Adventure beckons to you, and you begin to develop in ever-broadening circles. It is in this period that the early **fears of childhood need to be cleared away. Parents do not communicate very well with their children in the earlier years. When the child is in the process of learning the meaning of words, it is very easy for him to misinterpret and become afraid of things that he does not understand.**

The child starts from the status of being a little animal, and, as he develops, he has to be humanized and socialized. Now, the humanization process is very largely carried out in the early years of family living, before he goes to school. School then takes over and carries on the socialization process.

Families can be sick, in the same way as individuals. Does that surprise you? Well, it's true. Furthermore, there are early symptoms of family sickness, just as there are early symptoms of a cold coming on. You know when a cold is on the way, before you actually get the sniffles. You have a headache. There are pains in your neck. You feel all dragged out. In short, you know you're getting sick. Well, the things a person needs to do when he begins to get sick from a cold are known to all of us. We go home and go to bed and take care of ourselves.

We can't go deeply into the early signs of family sickness, just now. This subject alone would take a whole lecture. But, in general, such sickness involves the weakening of family ties. The diagnosis of whether a family is sick or well can usually be made from the answers to a few key questions. Have the family members *love and concern* for one another? Is *quarreling and dissension* in the family the rule or the exception? To what extent are there *joint* family projects or activities? Are *responsibilities and the meeting of problems* shared with the children, so that they can feel themselves participants rather than onlookers? What *values* are important to the family?

Parents might well give this matter of *values* a second look. If father and mother follow one set of standards for themselves, but prescribe another for their children, this is going to mean that the children acquire the values of the parents, rather than the ones prescribed for them. If papa is telling them to be honest, but is bragging about some shady business deal he has maneuvered—well, this simply will not go over with the kids. They'll know what's really going on, because they are keen observers and severe critics of their parents.

It is interesting that psychiatrists are beginning to think about mental sickness in terms of family sickness. They are increasingly treating the whole family, when one of the children or one of the parents gets sick mentally, because the individual member cannot stay well if the family is sick. If family wellness can be achieved, however, then the patient is likely to get well of his own accord.

The importance of the family as a haven of love cannot be overemphasized. What is love? Well, it's certainly something that you are not going to find out much about from my words here, because it's something which has to be felt and lived. Actually, the definition of love that appeals to me most is the one given by Erich Fromm in his book, *The Art of Love.* He gives four elements of love: care, responsibility, respect, and knowledge.

After all, you can't love a person without *caring* for him. And, if you care for him, you will feel *responsibility;* that is, you will have the ability to respond to him. And, if you feel responsive in this way, then automatically you have *respect.* To respect a person is not possible without *knowing* him. Care and responsibility would be blind, if they were not guided by knowledge.

All of us need love. And yet, if we're going to

have love, we must find it in an atmosphere of freedom with reference to the person we love We can't *make* anybody love us. All that we can to is to try to give of ourselves freely, without any strings attached. When we give our love to another person in this way, it engenders their love for us. This is the magic of love. It is something which you can't bargain for. You can't buy it. But, you can achieve it for yourself, if you give it to others.

There are various kinds of love within the family. Erotic love is very necessary because without it we wouldn't pass on our heredity to our race. And this, consequently, is something that Mother Nature has taken care of, by giving us the urge to mate and to live together as men and women. But it is just as important that Mother Nature also gave to woman the capacity for mother love. In the early months of infanthood, it is the mother's tenderness, her complete generosity to her baby, her willingness to do anything at all that this child of hers requires, which enables the child to feel secure in a very hostile outer world.

What about the father's love? Well, that becomes important a little later. As the child begins to explore his outer world, papa is the one who is the best interpreter of that. So, father love begins to be important in the last months of the first year, and until the child goes to school. Thereafter, it usually keeps its importance from the standpoint of interpreting.

There is also the love of the child for his parents and brothers and sisters, and between family members and more distant relatives.

In closing, I'd like to leave this thought with you. Love is the most vital force in our society.   The family circle is probably the only place where love takes hold within the early life of a person in such a way as to make it a part of his mature life, later. Love, response, and trust—these are the qualities which set mankind apart.   It is important to our Nation and to our world that we have well families, which will instill and cherish these qualities in their children, so that they, in turn, may be well.

23. COMMUNITY WELLNESS

A talk on community wellness ought to follow the one on family wellness. At least, it's pretty difficult to see how you can have really well families unless you have an environment that is conducive to wellness.

I have used the words "community wellness" quite deliberately, rather than "community health." This is because community health has come to have a specialized meaning to health people who have worked in this field for a good many years. To them, a healthy community usually means one that has proper sanitation, good water supply, some space, and which, in general, can be considered healthly from the standpoint of what people eat and drink.

Now, the social welfare people look at it a bit differently. They think of a community as a healthy community that doesn't have too much crime in it, where families aren't on relief, and that sort of thing. And, the economist looks at a community from the standpoint of whether the families are economically able to support themselves, or whether it is a healthy place for business. But, I'm thinking of community wellness as all of these things, plus a great deal more.

A community must not only be a healthy community sanitationwise, but it must be a place that promotes wellness in terms of families and wellness in terms of individuals. Children need a small, miniature world, in which to find out about the broader world into which they're emerging. If they can do their exploring in a small and friendly world, then later, when they become adult individuals and take their place in the larger world, they are more likely to work toward wellness at a broader level.

I'd like to tell you about a talk which I gave at Hofstra College a few months ago, when it was celebrating its 25th Anniversary. Hofstra College is located in Nassau County, Long Island, New York. I was asked to talk on the subject of the Long Island Community in 1985—how well-being within the community might be achieved and maintained; to look at what it was like 25 years ago, and what it is like now; then by projection to see what the picture is likely to be, 25 years from now.

Well, this subject was very interesting to me, because the population explosion that we are now experiencing is hitting Nassau County about as severely as any place in the country. This county was, at least until several years ago, the most rapidly growing county in the whole country. The eminent population expert, Philip Hauser, of Chicago, notes that we are already beginning to see the emergence of great strip cities, and predicts that, by 1985, one of them will stretch from Boston to Washington—a distance of over 400 miles.

Now, this simply means that well-being in Nassau County in 1985 will have to be achieved within an urban situation of very high density. To think of Nassau County in terms of an area as crowded as New York City rather shocked my audience. I said, "If you wish to achieve well-being for all—for families, for infants and children, for young people and old people, for the different racial groups—you've got *to plan for it* within a dense urban situation."

Can we get well-being under these circumstances? That is the problem.

Out of that discussion—out of the talks that have followed since, has come the realization that we need to ask some very basic questions about the way we build our cities. If we want to have well communities, they need certain things within them that most of our communities do not now have. First of all, a community needs a place where you can be a pedestrian—where you are not all tangled up with automobile traffic and dodging dangerous situations. How can we construct communities which are urban and yet which, at the same time, are protected from the automobile? This is a real problem, because people need to be able to get from one place to another quickly, and the automobile is a very useful tool as long as there aren't too many of them on the road at the same time. Yet, it involves considerable wear and tear for a commuter, with his office located inside of the city, to undergo the stresses and strains of automobile travel for several hours each day to get to and from work.

Many commuters in the New York City area are occupied in travel for as much as four hours a day. This time, added to eight hours of sleep, means that half of their lives are involved with either sleep or travel. It's just not the way to spend a life! So, question No. 1 is, how can we become pedestrians again within a dense urban situation?

It seems to me that question No. 2 is, how can we keep some havens of beauty within our living? How can we keep some wildlife around us? How can we enjoy the birds and the small beasties, which are a normal part of our environment? Are we going to let our urban design squeeze out of our life all these other living things? If so, we're going to remove from our children some of the important natural elements—important to both their aesthetic and their learning processes.

It would seem that one of our objectives in community design should be to produce communities which are little worlds, little replicas of the larger world into which our children will graduate as they move into adult life and job activities. Now, if this little world is to be representative of the larger adult world, it cannot be of too specialized a type. It can't be a community designed just for the leading young executives, for instance, or for a particular class of people. It ought to involve different kinds of people. It ought to involve different age groups. It ought to be a place where old people can, in a casual, normal way, mingle with the youngsters, because age and youth need each other.

A lot of the interest in life comes to the older person through enjoyment of the younger life, through entering its problems, and giving it some advice from time to time. And, a great deal of the future of a youngster depends upon his exposure to the wisdom of his elders. A properly designed community will foster this sort of interchange.

If we're going to cut down the amount of daily travel to and from our jobs, then industry needs to decentralize. We know that communities rather like to have some industry around, because it helps out on the taxes. Of particular interest in this respect is the beginning development of the so-called industrial parks which maintain some space and beauty around them, and at the same time, give the community a ready source of jobs close by.

Clearly, the key to this whole matter of community wellness is planning, and planning is something that we have not done very well in this country. We are so devoted to private enterprise as a concept—and a very real one—that we have wanted to go our own way regardless of consequences to others. Frequently, this has defeated the greater benefits that planning could have brought to our broader pattern of living.

I have recently become much impressed by the work of the Pratt Institute Architectural School, which is located in Brooklyn. This institute takes its graduate architectural students and assigns them, for their master's thesis, a joint problem to work on. There are 50 to 75 such students each year at the school. The problem assigned to them differs, from one year to another. For example, one year they worked on laying out Long Island as a unit; another year, on Staten Island. Another time, it was the New Jersey flats, an area of some 10 miles by 5 miles; and this last year, it was the 200 miles of the New York City river front, the harbor section.

Always, the students have had an objective, and an assignment. The method followed is to divide up the area involved into smaller areas, and to send each student into one small part of the total area, with a checklist of things that he should find out. The data are then pooled, and the entire class is given the problem of creating architectural designs suitable for the area, and producing the end result described by the objective. This is a wonderful way of working, and has produced some dramatic presentations of possibilities for the future.

Individual wellness and family wellness, and the possibility to attain them, will be enormously enhanced when we have community wellness. Let us, therefore, add this subject to our "must" list for work at the local level. While the nature of the solutions will vary considerably, according to the locality, the problems toward which such work should be directed are more or less common to all parts of the world.

24. ENVIRONMENTAL WELLNESS

In this talk, we shall consider "Environmental Wellness." Now, I admit that sounds rather strange as a title, because usually we do not think of an environment as well or sick. However, it is my feeling that if we are going to have individual wellness, family wellness, and community wellness we must have these kinds of situations develop within an environment *conducive* to wellness.

There are three questions to which I shall address myself. What does environmental wellness mean? What is man's attitude toward nature? And, how can we bring about environmental wellness?

Now for the first question: What does environmental wellness mean?

The title "environmental wellness" stems from my desire to distinguish it from the very commonly used title "environmental health." Environmental health has become identified primarily with such things as air and water pollution, and with radiation and occupational hazards. These are very real and important problems, and ones which affect the health of human beings.

Many of us know, for instance, about the disgraceful pollution of our rivers. That we are dumping sewage and commercial waste into the streams all over the country. That in some instances these streams become practically open sewers, and are blighting the areas through which they run. That they kill off the wild life dependent upon them, and are hostile to human life on their banks.

We are also becoming increasingly aware of the pollution of our atmosphere, as we struggle with the smog which infests more and more of our great cities; and of atomic fallout which threatens the heredity passed on to our children.

But environmental wellness is something more than a struggle against such evils.

Perhaps I can best describe what I mean by a well environment as against a sick environment by quoting from a provocative article in the *Saturday Evening Post* of January 28, 1961, entitled "The Battle to Save the Trees." The author, Charlton Ogburn, describes a 60-acre tract, mostly forest, near a proposed park at Springfield, Virginia, in these terms:

> "When I first saw this forest, it was an intricate community of oaks, dogwoods, orchids,

mosses and lichens, squirrels, mice, woodpeckers and moths; its spongy topsoil teemed with microscopic organisms. On my next visit, a few days later, nothing remained but some piles of charred, slowly burning tree stumps. A shopping center was going in there." [11]

Now, I suppose many of you in my audience have seen examples of choice tracts of wooded land or wildlife habitats plowed under and destroyed in this way, in the name of progress. Certainly, the environs of all of our great cities are replete with examples.

Let us ask, then, our second question: What is man's attitude toward nature and toward other forms of life?

Most of us living in this day and age have been brought up to consider the world as our oyster. We think of nature as something to be exploited. We think of ourselves as the dominant life form, and, consequently, we lord it over all the rest of the animal kingdom.

Now, it is true that the problem of survival is a basic one, and we must sometimes kill other forms of life in order to preserve our own. But, since man participates in his own evolution and since he has the capacity to direct the course of his own social development, there is no reason why he cannot face, on a more rational basis than he now does, the solution to those of his problems which involve nature.

One thing we must recognize. Regardless of the dominant position of man, he does not create the natural laws. He must obey them. Somehow, man must grow out of this strange psychology of life, that he must conquer nature by destroying it, and must learn instead to cooperate with it.

Let's look at this problem of conservation of natural resources. Conservation is not a very popular word in our society. I recall a time, a few years ago, when I attended an advisory committee session which was considering plans for the future of America. The matter of conservation came up and was shrugged off by most members of the committee. Why bother about conserving natural resources? There would always be other things that we could invent and use. The fact that the substitutes almost invariably would have a higher price tag did not enter the considerations at all.

When it came to the matter of how far ahead we should plan, the majority of the group thought that 25 years ahead was very, very long, and most were willing to settle for 5 years. A few of us held out for long-term planning. The chairman of the group was quite impatient with us and tried to pin us down to a specific number of years. Finally, in exasperation, he voiced what he considered an absurdity, "Well, Dunn, do you think we should pan as far ahead as one hundred years?" My answer was, "Yes, if we expect to be a great nation at that time."

During the whole history of civilization, it has been the aim and purpose of man to get along with nature and its great forces in any way that he could. With the advent of science, man has found it possible to subdue many of the forces of nature and bend them to his will. But, the time has now come for a revision of our concept of the benefits and responsibilities of holding domain.

We speak of conquering nature or of subduing rivers as though they were our enemy. But nature has been designed so as to maintain balance among different groups of its living things. If the number of any living species, for instance, tends to increase out of proportion, some force will rise to control it. Nature's law does not command us to do or to refrain from doing anything. It merely states that if a living being does so and so, then the result will be such and such. Balance requires checks. In our actions which involve nature, we must cooperate with her so that proper checks and balances can be maintained.

How silly this business of ruthless exploitation is! In order to make a quick profit, we act destructively and irresponsibly, and then for years others have to pay the price of the damage done.

Take the matter of pure air, for instance. Surely, pure air is everybody's gift from nature. It is all about us, all the time, or so we say. And yet, where can we find pure air any more? It's practically nonexistent over the inhabited parts of the earth. Why must man spoil so much of what he touches?

What is pollution anyway? Did you know that it is simply unused energy? That's all—whether it's water pollution, or air pollution, or radiation, or other. The amount of pollution that we have is largely a measure of our inexperience and our ineptitude in the engineering sciences. There isn't any reason at all, for instance, why we can't have an automobile engine that uses practically all of the hydrocarbon energy within the fuel, instead of throwing it out into the air to create smog. And, likewise, we really have no right to use atomic energy until we can find a way to utilize it all. The wastes that we are dispersing are extraordinarily dangerous to life everywhere, and to mankind in particular.

A vital component of environmental wellness is space. Man is beginning to find his living space uncomfortably crowded. In moving out over the earth's surfaces, he is tending to strip away everything in his path, over-expanding his civilization and his urbanization. This is gradually wiping out other life forms.

The English anthropologist, Piddington, estimates that at least 30 major life forms have been eliminated from the world in the last 50 years. On the whole, these are the larger life forms, the ones that can be killed with high-powered rifles. When I spoke of this to a friend from Alaska not long ago, he said,

"Well, I can add another to the list that you've mentioned, and that's the white polar bear. We find that it's very fine sport to chase the white polar bear with high-powered rifles from a helicopter. It's perfectly safe, you see. Although it is now illegal, the practice still goes on, and there is simply no place left for the white polar bear to go. It's just a question of time until he will be extinct."

I wish that there was time for us to look at other examples of this wantonness of mankind toward nature's other life forms. It is a sad commentary on our civilization that our whole tendency seems to be to exploit nature for a quick profit, and to kill our way toward dominance over the rest of the animal kingdom.

But we must get on, with the third question: How can we bring about environmental wellness? Perhaps one way might be to develop interest in biology on a really vast scale, so that it could become of major interest to all mankind. This would mean acquiring a deep interest in life—in the life process itself. After all, man stands at the apex of the pyramid of life, and he really should be the responsible guardian of the life process. He should be able to understand all life forms and their signficance. Perhaps, as suggested in an earlier talk, we could have a biological century of research, more or less like the geophysical year which was so successful. I am sure it would be a fascinating and exhilarating

experience—something we could carry on coopera-
tively with persons in other countries.

A further contribution to environmental wellness
would result from the stimulation of interest in
aesthetics—in the preservation and enhancement of
beauty, whatever its form. As Louis Bromfield
brings out in his book *Pleasant Valley*, the aesthetic
qualities of nature bring a particular joy and growth
and development to children.

> "Wherever they go in after life, they will
> possess the knowledge of the fields and the bril-
> liant beauty of the cock pheasant soaring above
> the green of a meadow in October. They will
> know how things grow and why. They will
> understand what goes on above the earth and
> in it." [12]

At an "earthy" level, a tremendous impetus in the
field of aesthetics, for example, could result from a
very simple type of program which could be carried
on at every level of social organization, beginning
with the home and family. I refer to a concerted
series of activities to eradicate "litterbugging," which
has become a national disgrace along our highways
and byways, in our parks, and almost everywhere
that people come together.

As parents, we must become aware, and make our
children aware, of the ugliness created by man's
litterbug habits; and we must exercise an active concern and even passion to change this attitude of
human indifference to one of personal responsibility

and pride in maintaining cleanliness and beauty in our surroundings.

If mankind is to be well, he must have an environment which is conducive to wellness. If we are to be the guardians of nature, each of us must try to be a respected guardian, obeying the rules himself.

Ultimately, environmental wellness is dependent upon social wellness, which is the subject of the next lecture.

25. SOCIAL WELLNESS

Social wellness is our topic for today. We have discussed individual wellness, family wellness, community wellness, and environmental wellness. Whether or not we have wellness in these various areas depends very greatly upon whether we can have social wellness. I can just hear someone in this audience saying: "Dr. Dunn, we could certainly use a little more social wellness. Every time a fellow picks up the newspaper, these days, he wonders what new 'sensational' is going to be in the headlines."

Well, it is a sick world. I think we have to admit that. Personally, it seems to me that it will go on being a sick world so long as we insist on balancing force with force, and bomb with bomb. I think we're going to have to learn how to fight *for* something instead of just fighting *against* things, all the time. Of course, if we had an invasion from outer space, all the peoples of the world would probably join in fighting against the invader.

But there is an alternative. If we can find a goal sufficiently broad and sufficiently important so that it embraces all of mankind, then we *can* join with our enemies and with the neutrals in fighting for that goal. This would give us a road to world peace.

In considering social wellness, I would like to discuss three aspects: What social wellness is; why it is essential to have social wellness; and what we can do to achieve social wellness.

Now, what is social wellness? Basically, the same definition for high-level wellness that we applied to the individual would apply also to high-level wellness for society. This definition, in fact, is applicable to all types of social organizations—to the family; to the community; to social groups such as businesses and political groups, religious organizations, and the like; to the nation; and finally, to the world of mankind itself. For all of these aggregates, it implies a forward direction in progress, an open-ended expanding future, and integration of the social aggregate into a total social personality.

Why is it that social wellness in this sense is essential to individuals in the various stages of their life cycle, to families, to social groups such as school and work, to communities, and to nations? The reason is that the condition of each larger social group affects the smaller groups within its sphere of influence. This is even true of the creative acts of those organizations and of the persons concerned with them. The creative imagination of the individual tends to follow the polarized lines of force of the physical environment in which he finds himself, and the lines of influence of the social organizations in which he participates. Likewise, the smaller groups of men tend to follow the lines of force and influence of larger organizations of which they are a part.

Contraction of space within these various types of energy systems—whether social or physical—which occurs when the two poles of the energy field are brought closer together, intensifies the effect of the polarized lines of force. This is the reason why, if you want to prevent a fight between two individuals, or two nations, you must separate them with some space in between. You must give them a chance to talk to each other, to try to understand each other's point of view.

A boundary line between two hostile nations should be insulated, temporarily, so as to force to arbitration the issue involved. Once men get around the council table, something happens; there is give and take. That is why the United Nations Organization is so important.

For a moment, let's return to the cycle of life. We have seen how most infants start life under a mother's loving care, and through childhood enjoy the indulgence of a family group. As we leave the security of the home, our circle of acquaintance widens constantly and we have playmate groups; we go to school; we explore the community in all of its ramifications; and finally, we move into the outer world, made up of social groups which overlap and interpenetrate every phase of our life activity. Our lives are spent within the framework of social organizations, all of which have overlapping fields of influence—our church, our fraternal organizations, our labor unions, a host of others too numerous to mention.

Let's have a look at these groups that affect us so much. The family and the community are probably the most important, but we've already discussed them pretty well. What about the school? After all, school days take up a very considerable chunk of our total lifetime. A teacher may have a fine grasp of program, but, at the same time, he may not have the talent to impart this knowledge to the child. This makes the competence of the principal very important to the school, because it is the task of the principal to redistribute information, encourage teachers in their activities, help them to weigh alternatives, and give direction to their teaching. The school, therefore, must function as a unit. The children, in turn, sense and react to the degree of unity that there is in the school and in its faculty.

Systems of work organization are of particular interest to me. Perhaps that is because I've been running organizations for 30 years of my life. For a long while, it has seemed to me that, since all of us have to live within organization structures and must spend so very much of our time within work organizations, it is terribly important that these organizations should be run in the right way. By "right way," I mean so that individuals are able to find a considerable amount of self-fulfillment within the work which they are doing.

As I see it, you can run an organization in many ways, falling somewhere along the scale of two extremes. At the one extreme is the autocrat who dominates and gives orders through a chain of command. He controls people under him through a variety of techniques, such as training, conditioning, fear of reprisal, promise of rewards, and the like. At the other extreme is the leader who stirs and inspires his people as individuals to exercise their latent creative possibilities as free spirits dedicated to the objectives of the organization. The first extreme is authoritarian control; the second is leadership through maximizing the creative effort of the individual as a participant.

Personally, after long experience, I am convinced that in most situations a relatively free organization actually gets more work done and is more effective than one which is run too rigidly. A considerable degree of freedom pays off in dollars and cents, as well as in other ways.

I can't begin to do what I would like to on this subject of social wellness. However, I would like to point out the tremendous every-day importance to us of our national and international organizations. Forty or fifty years ago when I was a boy, they simply wouldn't have made any difference to us. The family, the community, the school, the church—those were the things that counted. But that is no longer so. The things that happen internationally can affect and do affect, directly, our lives and our families.

I would like to recommend that you read a study prepared in 1959 at the request of the Committee on Foreign Relations of the United States Senate, by the Stanford Research Institute. It is entitled: *United States Foreign Policy: Possible Nonmilitary Scientific Developments and Their Potential Impact on Foreign Policy Problems of the United States.* The report is only a hundred pages long; but if you don't have the time to read it all, at least read chapter 2 which deals with "Science and National Sovereignty."

First of all, the report points out that national boundaries simply cannot stand in the way of solution of many international problems. The concept of national sovereignty of the air, for instance, is meaningless. The same is true for the oceans. Do we, for instance, as a country have any right at all to poison the upper atmosphere, which goes all over the world, with the explosion of our atomic bombs? And what about the dumping of our atomic waste matter into the oceans? We don't know what we are doing to the oceans, but we do know that whatever it is will affect other nations as well as our own. And what about weather control? We're talking about it, but we can be sure that if we do something to improve our own weather we're very likely to make worse some other fellow's weather.

The long and short of it is that social wellness, in a world that has shrunk as ours has, simply cannot exist for one group unless it exists for all groups. We must come to grips with social wellness on a world basis. There is no alternative.

High-level wellness for society requires that we consider people everywhere, and not just ourselves. I think that Dr. Brock Chisholm probably puts this as neatly as anyone I know when he says:

> ". . . for the first time in human history, the unit of survival is no longer the individual, the family, the group, the tribe, or the nation—it is the human race. For the first time we are in a situation where, if we expect to survive, we must arrange for the human race to survive. We must arrange for all to survive, otherwise none of us will." [13]

In other words, we had better get social wellness "or else."

Now, what can you and I do to help achieve social wellness? Well, I think that social wellness is everybody's business. Each of us must become true participants—not just onlookers—in the groups of which we are a part. Family and community life offer all of us such opportunities. When situations involve elements calling for our particular talents, we can use those talents and can stimulate others to action, whether or not we are in charge of things.

All of us have our own particular spheres of interest and influence. It is our responsibility to take part in promoting social wellness within these spheres of daily activity. The well-being of society depends upon the "you's" and "me's" who make it up.

26. RESEARCH ON WELLNESS

My talk today deals with research on wellness. All of us know the tremendous power of research. It is a beam of light that we focus on almost everything important that we wish to do. If we want to develop this area of high-level wellness as an area of broad interest to man and society, we must employ the great power of the research tool.

In this talk, I would like to discuss three things: some of the difficulties involved in doing research on wellness; some points of attack at which we might direct research in wellness; and the question, how do we go about getting support for research in wellness?

Let's look at the first item: What are the difficulties of doing research in wellness? Well, my answer would be, for one thing just plain lack of interest. I've said before in this series, and I would like to repeat, that we have become so very engrossed in doing the necessary job of patching up all sorts of things

that are wrong with man and with his social structure that we fail to see that this is only a part of the
problem. If we could stimulate interest and concern
in the *wellness,* rather than so predominantly in the
sickness, of man and of society, we would have in
our hands the means to prevent the very conditions
which we are trying to cure.

But, lack of interest is no more difficult to combat
than is the difficulty we face in *measuring* wellness.
After all, we have not clear-cut means of determining
when an individual *is* well. We can determine when
he is *not sick;* but how can we tell when he is really
performing at high potential?

Perhaps we could take a lesson from the automobile manufacturer as he designs and tests a new car.
Among his tests, of course, are numerous tests upon
the materials which he uses in the car. Then as he
develops various parts of the car, he does functional
tests upon these parts to see how well they operate.
In the end, he actually takes a car and puts it upon
a course, and runs it under all sorts of difficulties to
see how the car as a whole stands up. This is what
is called a performance test.

Now, in our medical assessment of patients, we
have a great many tests that are more or less akin to
the material tests. They tell us how a patient is at
the particular moment in terms of his blood analysis,
urine analysis, blood pressure, and the like. And we
have a substantial number of functional tests. For

instance, we can inject glycogen into the blood stream to find out how the kidneys handle it.

But, we do not have in medicine anything that's analogous to the performance test. We do not wear a person out to see how durable he is! The only performance test that we can apply to human beings is that of living over a period of years, and finding out how the person stands up to the wear and tear of life. Longevity might be considered such a performance test, particularly if it is associated in the older years with high productivity and a state of well-being. A group of oldsters between 80 and 90, for instance, who are alert, well, active, and participating in many ways in their social structure, undoubtedly should be classified as enjoying high-level wellness.

Now, it is easier to make an assessment of the wellness of a social organization than of an individual. Economic wellness is assessed in terms of a variety of measures of productivity, such as the employment index, the gross national product, and various other types of economic indices.

It is not so easy to assess cultural wellness. I suppose we could develop some measurements in terms of persons active in the arts, volume of visits to the museums, etc.; but actually, such criteria would not be of sufficient depth to give us a real understanding of cultural wellness—whether it is developing, growing, improving.

My own discipline is statistics. So, as you can well

imagine, I'm very much interested in measurement of things, and have been doing what I could in the past two or three years to try to find ways of measuring or "quantifying" wellness. Some of the answers are beginning to emerge. For one thing, the type of statistics we need for this purpose must be along a time axis. Individuals and their families are flowing through time more or less like a river flows along its stream bed. A census periodically provides a description of a cross section of the river. We repeat the census once every ten years so as to be able to see how the characteristics of the river are changing.

In modern times, we're developing some very fine sampling procedures which allow us to dip into the river at various crucial points and find out certain types of information. However, we do not have any real body of statistics that follows individuals and families through time. Yet that is exactly what we need for the study of human genetics, for instance. In genetics, we need kinship data that follow people through the years and ultimately tell us what happens to their children.

When an engineer studies a river, if he studies it long enough, he will come to know the velocities and directions of its various currents. He will be able to know exactly what should be done to the river at a particular point in order to redirect its course further along—to dig a channel somewhere in its future course, or to make a cove or harbor.

We can develop longitudinal statistics along a time axis, which will permit us to direct the flow of humanity in this way. A new type of preventive medicine can emerge—a preventive medicine which will help us to direct the flow of events and which will allow us to take, in time, those steps necesasry to prevent people from drifting into chronic disease.

These difficulties of conducting research in wellness and of measuring its magnitude should not discourage us. Actually, there are a number of promising points of attack which offer possibilities of breaking through such barriers. In this talk I would like to identify nine such points of attack for raising the levels of wellness. The time is too limited to go beyond simple identification.

1. Means of improving wellness in family living and in community living.

2. Measures to teach wisdom (in addition to, and as distinguished from, knowledge) within the present framework of education.

3. Measures to develop understanding and methods of adjustment in man's interpersonal relationships, throughout life.

4. Measures to develop higher levels of wellness among those in leadership positions with control over others.

5. Methods to ensure open channels of information and access to the reservoirs of knowledge, especially in controversial subjects.

6. Systematic and continued efforts to enhance the importance of creative expression throughout life and society.

7. Systematic and continued efforts to foster altruistic expression as a tonic to the spirit of man, and as a means of providing ego security among one's fellows.

8. Crystallization of the concept of maturity in wholeness, in all its ramifications.

9. Opportunity to utilize for the benefit of society those who have demonstrated maturity in wholeness and who have attained a high level of performance in their lives.

Let us now turn to the question: How do we go about getting support for research on wellness? I doubt whether this poses much of a problem, if we can find a way to excite the interest of people in well-being—that is, interest of the same type and intensity as that now directed at sickness and social breakdown. It is likely that most of the large categorical programs in the broad fields of public health—such as cancer and heart control programs, the mental illness and mental health programs, and the subjects of air and water pollution and of radiation contamination—will come eventually to incorporate within them substantial blocks of time, energy, and money for preventive aspects of these programs. Urban blight and urban renewal efforts, for example, can increasingly be transformed into urban planning and preventive programs to combat the social ills which afflict us.

Warren Weaver, in a January 1961 issue of *Science,* sums it up very nicely in these words:

> "We now know that science is intertwined not only with political and economic problems but with all the concerns of the humanists and artists. We now know that the mind and spirit of man approaches reality from many directions, appreciates order and beauty in many manifestations, and by joining all forces brings creative imagination and revealing insight to bear on all aspects of nature, of life, and of living." [14]

What greater challenge could there be to research than to explore this area of vital interest to all humankind?

27. A PERSONAL DISCIPLINE FOR WELLNESS

In this talk, I will pass on to you a personal discipline for wellness which has served me well. Actually, it has in it eight different ways that we can promote wellness within our bodies. The occasion for thinking through this list of eight points dates back several years.

You will recall that a few years ago there was considerable talk about relaxation of tension. Doctors were telling us that a good deal of our heart disease and mental disease was resulting from excess tension in life. Furthermore, we were beginning to realize that much of the hostility between groups of men and between nations was rooted in tension.

To me, this subject came into focus with the outbursts of violence which occurred in Egypt at Cairo, and in Hungary at Budapest.

In the development of various aspects of high-level wellness, I came to realize that ways of releasing tension had to be at the center of promoting high-level wellness, because better human relations are an essential element of high-level wellness.

The discipline discussed is not intended to embody a complete list of all the things we need to do in order to enjoy high-level wellness. It omits all of the ordinary things which are done to keep people well, such as measures to prevent disease, measures to ensure pure water and air and good nutrition, and, in general, the customary ways provided by medicine and public health to safeguard the health of the individual, the family, and the community. However, it does strike at the core of the problem in a different way. It does help us to integrate and reintegrate the self which, in turn, allows us to use the physical energies of our body wisely and to maintain the good relations needed in our every-day world.

Point 1 in this discipline is willingness to face inconsistencies in our thinking—to reexamine beliefs or practices in the light of contradictions which come to our attention, and, as needed, to readjust such beliefs or practices into an integrated and consistent whole, at some new level of adjustment and harmony.

You will find this point rather familiar, because it has been referred to in a number of our talks in this series. You will recall that in the talk on self, we brought out the confusion which exists in the minds of most of us between our self and our self-concept. If we insist upon clinging to a self-concept that is really foreign to our self, we lose touch with reality. Without facing up to reality, we cannot be well.

This recalls the old Greek maxim, "Know thyself," as the basis of good health. "Know thyself" may have been a luxury once, but today it is a necessity. Man can adjust himself to his changing environment only by knowing himself. Self-assurance or self-confidence comes through knowing one's true self. Understanding reality involves reassessing our beliefs when we are faced with inconsistencies.

Point 2 is willingness to hear and examine the other fellow's viewpoints with an open mind, in the interest of lessening tensions and promoting understanding.

In considering point 2, you will recall that when we were discussing values and value judgments, we said that the values and value judgments that we develop are gradually, over time, built into an assumptive form world. The way we conduct ourselves in the outer world depends very largely upon the information about the outer world which is stored in our inner world. This is also true of the other fellow. His actions, also, are predicated very largely upon his assumptive form world—how he perceives the world. So, the task of understanding another person involves trying to learn how he looks at the world, and in particular, how he sees us.

Point 3 is willingness to encourage freedom of expression from those around us, and particularly from members of the opposition.

We know, to start with, that we cannot understand the other person's assumptive form world unless we encourage him to talk. The other person has to be convinced that we *want* to hear his views and that we respect his views, whether or not we agree with him. Once we have listened to him, he is much more likely to give *our* views his attention.

The same holds between peoples of different nations. I've attended many seminars in this country on international questions, and almost invariably, even with a liberal audience, I find that they tend to be blind to how the persons of other countries see us. At times, I've wished that we could transform the TV program of Ed Murrow, "See It Now," into a program "See Yourself As Others See You." This would really do us a lot of good as a country.

Point 4 we shall term willingness to adjust our own views so as to arrive at an understanding with others, by searching for points of mutual agreement and, when possible, points of mutual inclusion in action programs.

This follows naturally if we have practiced points 1, 2, and 3. Point 4 will come of its own accord because we will find that it is easy and natural for us to adjust our own viewpoints. We are able to make this adjustment because we can see all sides of the situation.

Point 5 is willingness to make time for unhurried contacts with others when such relationships are essential, since seldom can understanding be cultivated in the rush of busy days.

Now the reason for point 5, of course, goes back to our talk on balance, and how very necessary it is to have relaxation and freedom from excessive tension if we are to achieve self-integration and group integration. The continuum of change so necessary to high-level wellness comes about almost spontaneously when we can maintain our self and our relationships with others in dynamic equilibrium.

Point 6 is willingness and determination to give credit and recognition to others when it is due them. To obtain recognition for achievements well done satisfies a deep need in the nature of all, and can lead to greater accomplishment.

Point 6 is a very practical one. It recognizes the great need of all men for human dignity. It is one thing that we can do for other people that doesn't cost us a thing and yet that brings to them great satisfaction. When we take credit that really belongs to another person, we are hurting ourselves. We cannot possibly enjoy a sense of personal dignity and personal integrity when we do this.

One word of caution. I am not advocating flattery. When we flatter people, they usually know that they do not deserve the praise. Credit should only be given when it is due.

Point 7 is eagerness and determination to serve others as opportunities arise, without expectation of direct or indirect personal gain. To perform such services for others establishes strong bonds of understanding and good will, and helps to refute the reputation of selfishness, avarice, or greed for power, so often deservedly attributed to individuals, groups, and nations.

This is, of course, altruism. You will recall that altruism is buried deep in our tissues, and, in fact, that the cells begin to practice cellular altruism as soon as they begin to form a cooperative commonwealth. The cells gave up part of their freedom of action in order to get a better living for all the cells. To practice altruism is a pretty good way to obtain a measure of security in this life of ours. When we give of ourselves freely to others—that is, when we practice altruism—it inspires gratitude on the part of others. They wish us well. And, this well-wishing accumulates like a trust fund. Dr. Albert Schweitzer is a living example of what I'm trying to say. He has given himself away all his life. Today he enjoys the gratitude and good wishes of all of the people of the world.

Point 8 is willingness to give freedom to those we love. When one loves, the strength of one's emotions tends to make him possessive of the object of his love.

Yet, to be possessive tends to block response from others. Unless one can conquer this tendency in himself, transforming possessiveness into unselfish service to the object of his love, tensions will mount, both within one's self and in his relationships with others, resulting in frustrations, hate, and cruelty.

Now, let us look at this personal discipline for high-level wellness, as a whole. It is very practical. It is not just a moral code. It is not a motto to be hung on the wall and looked at occasionally. It is something which must be lived, every day. It must become second nature.

The practice of this discipline will help you to maintain self-integration and a dynamic equilibrium of change so that you can face reality; so that you can know yourself; so that your body can enjoy high-level wellness; so that your mind is functioning well as a problem-solving mechanism; so that your relationships with others are at their very best.

28. A PHILOSOPHY CONSISTENT WITH WELLNESS

In this talk we shall discuss "A Philosophy Consistent with Wellness." All persons need a personal philosophy—that is, a way of life. And, all persons have one, although perhaps they do not recognize it as an explicit philosophy.

The nature of man requires that he must have a personal philosophy. Social organizations need a philosophy too. The family, the community, the work organization, the church, the nation—all of these must have a philosophy. And, in my opinion, a philosophy is very badly needed to encompass mankind as a whole, if we are to solve the problems of our day.

The creative imagination of the individual, which is the stabilizer of his awareness axis, tends to follow the guide lines of the social organization in which the person is a participant. Likewise, smaller groups of men, such as families or communities, tend to follow the energizing influence fields of larger organizations. This is the reason why a philosophy adequate to encompass mankind as a whole is needed, if we are to have peace in the world.

If a philosophy is to be meaningful, it must be consciously lived. It can't be a process of just giving lip service to something or other. It must be something which you try out, experience, and acquire self-confidence in doing.

Through the years, people have asked me the question, "What do you believe in, Dunn? So many of the things that you are saying require some sort of belief. What is behind them?" So eventually, I tried to capture my personal philosophy and put it down on paper. It's not an easy thing to do, and I am not saying that this philosophy which suits me very well is something that *you* should adopt. However, it has stood up well under test, especially during the last few years when these ideas on high-level wellness have been emerging and expanding very rapidly in my thinking. I have called my philosophy "Our World" and think of it as a synthesis of man's achievements, aspirations, and potential future. The whole philosophy is compressed into only two sentences, and is less than a hundred words in length. Here it is:

> "You, I, and our fellow men are emerging into a new world, our world. In this new world,

science, faith, and the destiny of man blend with the oneness of life in the alchemy of man's never-ending search for truth, as this search is carried on throughout society in an energy field of responsive awareness, love, and trust, and is directed toward improving the world for mankind as a whole."

I would like to spend the rest of the time trying to explain what these few words mean.

Each of the elements in the equation for this new world is essential for its formulation. We have to call it a *new* world because the various worlds of each of us must be replaced by the "our world" of all of us. We have to treat *our* world as a total social organization, not just as a confederacy of many independent social units.

Now a social organization, whether it is small or large, is made up of a group of individuals. It has an understanding of its own. It has a birth, a growth, and a maturity. There is a unity in organization which is more or less equivalent to a personal ego. An organization can feel satisfaction in a task well done. It can be proud of itself. It can develop confidence in its ability and its purposes. It has a spirit of its own, a spirit made from the blending of spirits of all of those who participate in it. And, we take pride in the achievements of our organizations of which we are a part. We like to say, when it has done something creditable, "Ah, this is my outfit." Or, "This is my nation." Well, that's what I want to see come about on a world basis. I hope that some day we can say with pride, "This is *our* world."

Let us return to the statement "in this new world, science, faith, and the destiny of man blend with the oneness of life in man's never-ending search for ultimate truth." The word "science" is indispensable because science is the keen-edged tool shaped to the hand and the mind of man. After all, clearly science is the principal element which has changed the world so radically—particularly within the last few decades. It has revolutionized communication and transportation, food habits, living habits. It has made the world a smaller place, a more crowded place.

Now, faith is a part of the philosophy because we cannot have peace of mind without a personal faith. Nor could we have self-confidence if we did not have faith in self. When we try out our understandings of what the outside world is like—our assumptive form world—and find that it works, the experience we gain brings us confidence in ourselves. It gives us courage to face the world and to adventure boldly.

This is a rational type of faith. It encourages us to face up to reality, to assess things as they are, ourselves included. Whether one's faith is a rational one of this type or a faith accepted as a belief from others, some sort of faith is essential. A person without faith in something is a ship without rudder.

Now, science, faith, and the destiny of man go together, because destiny, as I am using the term, is a creative type of destiny. It will emerge only as we free the creative spirit deep buried within man.

And the component "oneness of life" is in the philosophy because man shares with all living creatures a will to sacrifice and to fight for the survival of his kind. All life forms are children of energy. They live by the laws of energy, and man is no exception.

The words "ultimate truth" are in the philosophy because this is the goal toward which man reaches and in which his faith resides. He knows that the truth is there if he can find his way toward it. His destiny is to search for it.

The statement continues, "as this search is carried on throughout society in an energy field of responsive awareness, love, and trust and is directed toward improving the world for mankind as a whole." The reason for introducing society into the picture is because social change is imperative, and social groups must participate in the change if it is to be acceptable to them.

"Responsive awareness, love, and trust" are in the statement because these are the vital forces which bind man to his fellows. And because response becomes love, and love involves trust.

"Energy field" is included because this is the creative area of social action within which these forces can be exerted on an energy charge present and in balance.

When I refer to "mankind as a whole," I do so in the belief that this cannot be side-stepped. Man *is* a whole. Man *is* one race—the human race. And his strength lies in unity and in wholeness.

Why is the word "alchemy" in the philosophy? It is there because the transformation of man must take place in the crucible of a struggle, a struggle toward a common goal and for a common good.

As I said at the beginning of this talk, this philosophy is a personal one. The principal reason that I am stating it explicitly, for whatever value it may have to you, is that it is a philosophy which seems to be consistent with the concept of high-level wellness. Furthermore, it recognizes implicitly the two great mysteries of the universe mentioned in an earlier talk—the nature of energy, and the nature of consciousness. While these still remain mysteries to us, perhaps as suggested by Father Pierre Teilhard de Chardin, in his book *The Phenomenon of Man,* energy might be considered a tangential force and consciousness, a radial force. Whatever these forces are, they seem to permeate all types of matter and life in the universe, and, therefore, they should be implicit in a philosophy consistent with high-level wellness.

This new world that I am speaking of has already been born in the minds of men in various parts of the world. It can come to actuality gradually or quickly, depending upon the breadth and the depth of response that it finds in the hearts of men throughout the world, and upon the growth in numbers of people who dedicate themselves—their hands, their hearts, their material resources, and their creative energies—to its achievement.

Remember that high-level wellness involves direction in progress forward and upward toward a higher potential of functioning. It involves an open-ended and ever-expanding tomorrow with its challenge to live at a full potential. It requires the integration of our whole being—mind, body, and spirit—in the functioning process.

Each of us will struggle toward this goal in his own way and in his own sphere of interest and influence. In the process, it is likely that many will feel the need to make their personal philosophy of life more consistent with these aims. I hope that in this talk you may find something useful for your purposes.

29. THE DIGNITY OF MAN, RELATIVITY, PURPOSE, AND HUMAN DESTINY

This talk, on "The Dignity of Man, Relativity, Purpose, and Human Destiny," is the last in our series on high-level wellness for man and society. I have chosen this very "high-sounding" title, not because I expect, in fifteen minutes, to develop any of these profound components in depth, but because I would like to point out to you the interrelationship between them.

Now, everything would seem to indicate that human destiny is reaching a decisive point, a point of no return. Over the centuries, man has been climbing a succession of great mountains. He has conquered them, one after the other, and his science has ascended to almost unbelievable heights in terms of his ability to control nature. However, he is now on a crest. He can go forward into a new type of creative destiny, or he can slip backward into the abyss of war. Total war, such as lies ahead of us if we elect the backward rather than the forward direction, might well mean the destruction of the human race, or, at least, of civilization as we now know it.

It is difficult for any of us to comprehend what the total war of the future means. We have had war as a part of our tradition, a part of our long-time history, and, consequently, in certain ways we tend to idealize it. We see war glorified on our motion picture screens. And, we are inclined to think of courage and heroism and the qualities brought out in the individual during these times of crisis as assets—to be chalked up to the credit of war.

However, war has now changed its character so completely, and the prospect of atomic war or bacteriological war is so devastating, that it is simply unthinkable as a way of resolving problems. Our feeling of safety because we can attack the enemy and devastate his country is a fragile shield at best. For, in devastating the enemy, most of us would die also. Brock Chisholm has summed it up in this way:

> "No nation, now or ever again, can defend its own people from death by attack. That era of the human race is finished. If anyone has any doubts on this point, even in relation to the hydrogen bomb, one needs only examine the biological possibilities. A group of civilians can use biologicals—with no navy, no army, no air force, no large numbers of people, no heavy in-

dustry—and destroy overnight the possibility of any country in the world making effective war without themselves being identified." [15]

If war is no longer a part of national policy, how in the world can we protect ourselves? Can we cling, for instance, to the concept of dignity of man which is being disrespected through many parts of the world but which is still the cornerstone of our faith?

The concept of dignity of man rests upon faith in man's worth as an individual. The phrase has come to mean that the individual must be free to pursue his self-fulfillment and his happiness as indispensable parts of life and that, consequently, man must be regarded by society as an end sufficient unto himself. He is not to be coerced by social pattern or design into the fulfillment of some other end, one prescribed by society.

The importance to civilization of this concept of the dignity of man rests on the fact that it nurtures the individual's uniqueness; that the individual, although he must live in a world made up of organizations, will find self-fulfillment as an individual only if he can express his uniqueness.

It is true, of course, that groups of individuals must also be strong. They must be efficient as groups in order to survive as organizations. Our nation must be strong. Our industry must be strong. Our communities and our families must be strong. And, many other types of social organizations must be durable enough to ensure that society survives.

In this country, we think that it is our enemies who are flouting the dignity of man concept. And, sure enough, they are. However, in certain respects we are almost as bad as they. Concerning this "organization man," of whom we've heard so much in our country, I would like to ask this question: Aren't the industrial man of the free world and the dialectical man of the communist world both just two types of representatives of organization man? "The vigor and the strength of the free enterprise system," says the industrial man, "depends upon co-operation and pulling together as a team." "The principle of individual liberty," says the Marxist, "prevents the solution of the problems facing society."

Actually, the dignity of man is being stifled both by industrial man and by dialectical man. Individuality of the industrial man is largely lost in the uniformity of the group. A society, patterned after the machine, is relatively insensitive to imagination and to spiritual adventure, love, and beauty. And dialectical man, since he is fashioned by the State from early childhood to fill his particular niche in its structure, is primarily oriented toward the social organization for his personal welfare, happiness, and life purposes.

It is my belief that the dignity of man is essential as a concept because it is part and parcel of high-level wellness. It is certainly a part of mental health. Personal dignity is essential for the realization of uniqueness and the successive reintegration of the individual. Likewise, the dignity of social groups— the family, the community, the school, the church— is essential for the maintenance of social well-being.

Man can take pride in his activities as social man only to the degree that he can maintain his own sense of personal dignity. As a creatively oriented individual, he can contribute more to his social group than he could possibly contribute simply as a cog in a machine which he serves.

We considered in a previous talk how uniqueness and conformity go hand in hand. All of us need to conform, in the sense of being responsible members of our social groups. But all of us also need to express our uniqueness. Perhaps some of us are better organizers than others, and some of us might be bolder adventurers. However, to a greater or lesser degree, both these qualities—uniqueness and conformity—exist in each of us all the time. The same is true of the cooperative commonwealth of cells which make up our bodies. Cells are intensely individualistic; yet, as I explained in an earlier talk, they are associated in a cellular commonwealth, and practice cellular altruism. They are willing to give up certain things so that they may participate in the common good of the whole.

The same thing is true of social organizations. Quite regardless of country or ideology, this polarity between individuality and conformity is man's link to the building and stabilizing energy forces of nature. His individuality represents a positive or a creative pole, while conformity represents a negative or a restrictive force. The whole is a social replica of the energy field. The lines of force of the energy field tend to give direction to the creative imagination of the individual—direction with meaning to society.

When a person can maintain his personal dignity within the social matrix, he finds it easier to reintegrate himself and to solve his problems. He is able to maintain a dynamic equilibrium which allows him to use fully the energies at his disposal. He is on the road to mental health and to high-level wellness.

In my talk to you on the emergence of the mind, I said that man is undergoing a rapid and transforming evolution of his mental powers. He seems to be breaking out of the limitations of conceptual consciousness into a much freer area of creative consciousness. It used to be that logical systems were thought of as more or less absolute in character. They were sharply defined and they were compartmentalized. Well, no longer do we consider them absolute. System after system of human knowledge is becoming fuzzy and blending one into another. Take, for example, physics and biochemistry, which are giving way to biophysics.

The creative consciousness which is emerging represents the development of imaginative thinking. It represents a progressive organization of interrelatedness into wholeness. Inevitably, then, relativity will replace absolutism in our thought processes. Just as relativity has proven to be a dynamic and a revolutionary force in connection with modern physics, so, in my opinion, it will come to be recognized as a dynamic in the *mental* evolution which is now under way.

And, as we proceed toward the higher strata of creative consciousness of which mankind is capable, it would follow that we will increasingly free ourselves from the shackles of time as a dimension. Time rules the physical world, and, in a way, it will always rule us, because we are tied to the physical world through our bodies. However, as we emerge into creative consciousness, purpose will increasingly modify time, and it will be possible for man to free himself from time to a degree, by substituting purpose for time, or perhaps by blending time and purpose.

In my own thinking, I have termed this type of future as "creative destiny," and have defined it as the ever-unfolding future that emerges before the individual, as he releases the creative imagination which is his heritage, and integrates his whole being through creative expression so as to fulfill the highest potential of which he is capable.

Now we can begin to see why the dignity of man, relativity, purpose, and human destiny are inter-related. They are interrelated because they represent functions of the highest order of human mentality—that order which is emerging as creative consciousness.

In the time remaining, I will try to summarize this talk and the series which it terminates.

Mankind is walking the ridge of a Great Divide. At any moment, he can topple into war and destruction, or he can emerge on a clear-cut path which leads toward a creative type of destiny. You may say: "But it takes so long to transform man. How can he possibly change quickly?" My reply would be that we are in one of those rare periods of history when transformations *can* take place with almost dramatic rapidity.

All of us are familiar with transition points in the scheme of things. Take water, for instance. At a certain temperature it turns to ice; at another, it turns to steam. The characteristics of water in these three conditions are entirely different. It is the same with the emergence of life, or the emergence of thought, on earth. After a long period of slow development, a gigantic advance is made, seemingly all at once. The world is never the same after such a transition.

Well, I think that is the kind of step we are in the process of taking now. It seems to me that what we are doing—and what we must do, if we are to survive as a race—is to bridge the gap between science on the one hand and our philosophy, our religions, and our way of life on the other. If we can bridge this gap, it will become just such a transition.

It is my firm conviction that the concept of high-level wellness can make a small contribution to this area of human destiny. And on that note, I bring this series to a close.

Notes to the Text

(For fuller information about the publications mentioned,
see the Bibliography.)

	Note	Page of ms. on which mentioned
(1)	World Health Organization, "Constitution of the . . .," preamble	1
(2)	Williams, Roger, *Free and Unequal*, p. 52	12
(3)	Selye, Hans, *The Stress of Life*, p. 66	19
(4)	Huxley, Julian, *Evolution in Action*, p. 47	67
(5)	———, *Man in the Modern World*, p. 60	67-68
(6)	Piddington, R. A., *The Limits of Mankind*, p. 32	75
(7)	Mumford, Lewis, *The Transformations of Man*, p. 4	80
(8)	Penfield, Wilder, "The Interpretive Cortex," *Science*, June 26, 1959, p. 1725	102
(9)	Cantril, Hadley (quoting Carl Rogers), *The "Why" of Man's Experience*, p. 33	112
(10)	Hayakawa, S. I., *The Semantic Barrier*, p. 2	129
(11)	Ogburn, Charlton, "The Battle to Save the Trees," *Saturday Evening Post*, January 28, 1961, p. 28	185
(12)	Bromfield, Louis, *Pleasant Valley*, p. 334	190
(13)	Chisholm, Brock, "The Expanding Concept of Public Health," *American Journal of Public Health*, Supp. to June 1960 issue, p. 92	199
(14)	Weaver, Warren, Introduction to "The Moral Un-Neutrality of Science," by C. P. Snow, *Science*, January 27, 1961, p. 255	207
(15)	Chisholm, Brock, "The Expanding Concept of Public Health," *American Journal of Public Health*, Supp. to June 1960 issue, p. 90	226-227

Bibliography

Suggested as supplementary reading for lectures specified.

Lecture

Alexander, Peter. *Atomic Radiation and Life.* First published 1957. London, Penguin Books Ltd. 239 pp. Pelican Book A-399. See particularly the material on cell biology 5, 9

Allport, Gordon W. *Becoming.* Basic considerations for a psychology of personality. New Haven, Conn., Yale University Press, 1955. 109 pp............... 4, 16, 29

Beck, William S. *Modern Science and the Nature of Life.* New York, Harcourt, Brace and Company, 1957. 302 pp. 9, 26, 29

*Bromfield, Louis. *Pleasant Valley.* First published 1945, Harper & Brothers. Cardinal edition 1954, C-138. 336 pp. 24

Brown, Harrison. *The Challenge of Man's Future.* An inquiry concerning the condition of man during the years that lie ahead. New York, The Viking Press, 1954. 290 pp. 10, 29

*Cantril, Hadley. *The "Why" of Man's Experience.* New York, The Macmillan Company, 1950. Second printing 1957. 198 pp. 15

Caplan, Gerald. *Concepts of Mental Health and Consultation: Their Application in Public Health Social Work.* Washington, D. C., U. S. Govt. Printing Office, 1959. 269 pp. Children's Bureau Publication No. 373 .... 7, 19, 22

Chapple, Charles C. "An Inquiry into Common Denominators of Cellular Theory." *Pediatrics*, Vol. 7, February 1951, pp. 269-293 5

Chardin, Pierre Teilhard de. *The Phenomenon of Man.* English translation with introduction by Julian Huxley. New York, Harper & Brothers, 1959. 318 pp. 11, 28

*Chisholm, Brock. "The Expanding Concept of Public Health." *American Journal of Public Health*, Supp. to June 1960 issue, Vol. 50, No. 6, pp. 88-94............... 25, 29

---

*Indicates sources from which matter has been quoted, with permission of author and/or publisher, as required.

Davenport, Russell W. *The Dignity of Man*. New
York, Harper & Brothers, 1955. 338 pp.   29
Dubos, Rene. *Mirage of Health: Utopias, Progress
and Biological Change*. New York, Harper &
Brothers, 1959. 236 pp. World Perspectives,
Vol. 22   1
Dunn, Halbert L. (Note: A fuller bibliography of
his writings bearing on high-level wellness is available from the author on request.)
————. "Creative Destiny." A philosophy of social
organization for civilized man based upon his crea-
tive genius and a process of day-to-day adjustment.
The Indian Journal of Political Science, Vol. XV,
No. 1, January-March 1954, pp. 50-57; *The Pharos*
of Alpha Omega Alpha Honor Medical Society, Vol.
17, No. 3, May 1954, pp. 22-28; *Journal of the National Medical Association*, Vol. 46, No. 3, May 1954,
pp. 193-197; Portuguese text in *Jornal do Comercio*
(Rio de Janeiro), June 5, 1955; part IV of *Your
World and Mine*, Exposition Press, 1956   28
————. "Social Change and the Fundamentals of Com-
munity Organization." *Journal of the American
Association for Social Psychiatry*, Vol. I, No. 1,
Fall 1959, pp. 11-20; *Journal of Educational Sociol-
ogy*, Vol. 33, May 1960, pp. 373-383 .... 10, 23
————. "What High-Level Wellness Means." *Cana-
dian Journal of Public Health*, Vol. 50, No. 11, No-
vember 1959, pp. 447-457 .... 1, 4, 21
————. "High-Level Wellness in the World of Today."
*The Journal of the American Osteopathic Associa-
tion*, Vol. 61, August 1962, pp. 978-987.   1
————. "A Philosophy for Community Development."
Community Development Seminar, University of
North Carolina School of Public Health, Depart-
ment of Health Education, May 5-9, 1963.   23
————. "A Positive View of Aging Asks Much of Edu-
cation." *School Life*, Vol. 46, No. 4, Jan.-Feb. 1964,
pp. 30-34.   18
Fromm, Erich. *The Art of Loving*. An enquiry into
the nature of love. New York, Harper & Brothers,
1956. 133 pp. World Perspectives, Vol. 9 .... 16, 22
Geldard, Frank A. "Some Neglected Possibilities of
Communication." *Science*, Vol. 131, No. 3413, May
27, 1960, pp. 1583-1588   13

Lecture

Mooney, Ross L. "Toward a Realization of the Elementary Conditions of Existence." Philosophy underlying creativeness in the sense of being, belonging, becoming, befitting. 1957. (Note: At present available only in mimeographed form.) 4

Moustakas, Clark E. Editor. *The Self: Explorations in Personal Growth.* New York, Harper & Brothers, 1956. 284 pp. A collection of articles. Contributors: Gordon W. Allport, Andras Angyal, Erich Fromm, Kurt Goldstein, Karen Horney, Carl G. Jung, Prescott Lecky, Dorothy Lee, A. H. Maslow, Ross L. Mooney, Clark E. Moustakas, Otto Rank, Sarvepalli Radhakrishnan, Marie I. Rasey, Carl R. Rogers, Jean-Paul Sartre, David Smillie, Rabindranath Tagore, Francis Wilson 16

Muller, H. J. "Our Load of Mutations." *The American Journal of Human Genetics,* Vol. 2, June 1950, pp. 111-176 9

*Mumford, Lewis. *The Transformations of Man.* New York, Harper & Brothers, 1956. 249 pp. World Perspectives, Vol. 7 11

*Ogburn, Charlton, Jr. "The Battle to Save the Trees." *The Saturday Evening Post,* January 28, 1961, pp. 28-29, 68-70 24

*Penfield, Wilder. "The Interpretive Cortex." *Science,* Vol. 129, June 26, 1959, pp. 1719-1725 14

*Piddington, R. A. *The Limits of Mankind.* A philosophy of population. Bristol, John Wright & Sons Ltd., 1956. 153 pp. 10

Poincaré, Henri. *The Foundations of Science.* Science and hypothesis; the value of science; science and method. Lancaster, Pa., The Science Press, 1946. 553 pp. 17, 18

Reiser, Oliver L. *The Integration of Human Knowledge.* A study of the formal foundations and the social implications of unified science. Boston, Porter Sargent, 1958. 478 pp. Extending Horizons Books 3, 13

Rogers, Carl R. "A Therapist's View of the Good Life." *The Humanist,* Vol. XVII, No. 5, September-October 1957, pp. 291-300 16

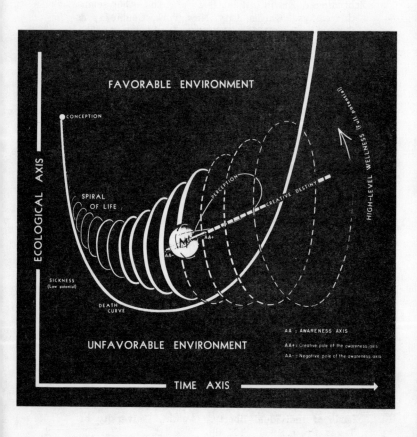

A MODEL OF MAN CONSISTENT WITH THE BIOLOGICAL BASIS FOR HIGH-LEVEL WELLNESS

The Model of Man conceptualizes man as a whirling globe (M), moving in a spiral course (the Spiral of Life), through time and through the environment (natural and social) from his conception to his death. Death is indicated as a Death Curve following the usual form of the death rate, which is high at the extremes (beginning and end) of life. The environment ranges from very favorable at the top of the model to very unfavorable at the bottom.

Man (M) is conceptualized as a manifestation of organized energy, an energy field spinning around an awarenes axis (AA)** between its two poles, of which AA+ represents the creative or positive axis, with abundant energy, and AA−, the negative axis, deficient in energy.

As M spins on his course, (the Spiral of Life) the AA+ pole of his axis optimally points towards the core of his projected Spiral of Life. The projected axis of this spiral, defined as creative Destiny **, involves an implicit trust by man in his creative imagination.

High-Level Wellness is the ever-changing, emergent side of the spiral traveled by man. Sickness or low level potential lies to the rear of the spiral.

The shell of the whirling globe M is perforated by many apertures facing in all directions (the intake-output ports for energy exchange and the perception outlets for the several senses of man). Perception is portrayed by the infinity symbol, ∞, to indicate that the process of perception is a continuous, flowing process, inside-outside and outside-inside. Perception extends farther outward (imagination) and penetrates more comprehensively inward (insight) when experienced near the AA+ pole.

The part of this process located within man is conceptualized as a neuromusuclar complex, incorporating within it emotional, muscle-tension patterns, as well as other types of memory, the whole being the mind of man. Values are built by experience recorded within this complex. Love emerges through responsive awareness, disclosure of the inner self, communication, understanding and interdependence.

It is conceived that when fixed beliefs and social pressures are exerted upon man sufficient to force the AA+ axis to turn away from the creative-destiny projection of this axis, the full potential of M becomes lowered and wellness lessened. Also, that when the AA+ pole is forced to the AA− position, the integration of M tends to dissolve rapidly as an energy organization into its component parts, resulting in death (as, for example, in cases of extreme debility from chronic disease, coupled with lack of the desire to live).

All that the Model of Man portrays for the individual can also be extended to man's social institutions (family, community, nation, or mankind as a whole), substituting the particular institution in the place of M and incorporating individuals as the units of the particular social organization.

The creative imagination of the individual tends to follow the polarized lines of force of the physical environment and of the social organizations in which he is a participant. Likewise the smaller groups of men tend to follow the lines of force of larger organizations of which they are a part. Contraction of space within these various types of energy systems intensifies the effect of the polarized lines of force.

Awareness Axis is the dynamic balance of an integrated self which is maintained as a moving axis of equilibrium between the various energy fields which affect the individual from within and without.

** *Creative Destiny* is the ever-unfolding future that emerges as one releases the creative imagination which is his heritage, and integrates his whole being through creative expression to fulfill the highest potential of which he is capable.

BIOGRAPHY

A strong believer in interdisciplinary exploration, Dr. HALBERT L. DUNN has recently entered upon his fifth career—that of lecturer and consultant in high-level wellness. This he regards as a culmination and fitting-together of the "learnings" gleaned along the way, as teacher, physician, vital statistician, and administrator of various organizations. Never an indivivdual to be easily categorized, he has with insatiable curiosity and the unshakable certainty that "everything is inter-related," ranged the territory and written in the fields of: anatomy, physiology, medicine, hospital statistics, vital and health statistics, human relations, aging, and organization and administration at local, national, and international levels.

In pursuing this his fifth career, Dr. Dunn is convinced that *Education*—in the family, the school, and at all the other points in a person's life where it is accessible—is the principal "open sesame" to high-level wellness. He regards the present book as an opening thrust in this direction.

In the area of biographical specifics, the following selections of background and experience indicate some of the influences which have undoubtedly contributed to the views, interpretations, and philosophy expressed by the author in the present book:

Born 1896, New Paris, Ohio. M. D. 1922, and Ph. D. 1923, University of Minnesota. Assistant in medicine, Presbyterian Hospital, New York City, 1923-24. At Mayo Clinic, Rochester, as fellow in medicine, 1924-25, and as chief of statistics, 1929-32. At Johns Hopkins University, 1924-29, teaching biometry and vital statistics. Directed the University Hospital and taught medical statistics, University of Minnesota, 1932-35. Chief of the National Office of Vital Statistics, 1935-60 (originally under the Bureau of the Census, later under the U. S. Public Health Service); special assistant on aging, U. S. Public Health Service, 1960-61. Retired June 1961, to pursue high-level wellness work.

Secretary General of the Inter American Statistical Institute, 1941-52; member of the Advisory Panel of Experts on Health Statistics, World Health Organization, 1951-61.

Throughout the years, Dr. Dunn's work activities have involved foreign travel to a number of countries—in Europe, South and Central America, Mexico, and Canada. He was chairman of the U. S. Delegation for at least four of the numerous international conferences which he attended. In both the United States and abroad, he has lectured extensively, and his writings have appeared in a wide variety of professional journals.

Index